A happy, healthy you

Caroline Yeats

Text and recipes by Caroline Yeats

Illustrations by Lisa Huxley-Blythe

Photography by Caroline Yeats and friends

Designed by Loulou Clark

Edited by Tara O'Sullivan

Published 2020

ISBN 978-1-5272-5574-6

The content of this book includes personal opinions of the author. The author is a qualified nutrition practitioner, having studied for a Diploma of Naturopathic Nutrition at the College of Naturopathic Medicine, London from 2016 to 2019. Please note that the information in this book is for informational purposes only. It should not be considered as medical advice and is not intended to diagnose, prescribe, treat or cure any medical condition. Please consult your doctor if you have any health concerns.

A happy, healthy you

Caroline Yeats

For Oscar:

I hope your life is filled with happiness.

Love you forever,

Mummy xxx

Contents

'You never know how strong you are until being strong is the only choice you have'

– Bob Marley

Introduction:

My story

I'm Caroline. I'm a mum, a wife, a nutritionist, a very driven person, and a lover of food and yoga. I'm passionate about health and well-being and I've spent the past few years transforming myself from a stressed businesswoman into a balanced and happy person in love with life. But that life changed for good when I was diagnosed with incurable stage IV cancer in September 2018. I was 33, in great health, so I thought, and my son was only a year old.

I've written this book to share my story and the lessons I've learned along the way that are helping me live a happy and healthy life despite what I'm going through. Whatever challenges you have in your life, be they chronic illness, stress or the general strains of day-to-day living, I hope you can find inspiration and tips to help you live a happy and healthy life, too.

March 2016: I was a recently married, highly successful career woman living and working in central London. In so many ways I had an incredibly perfect life. A challenging, interesting, highly paid job that involved plenty of world travel, often staying in fancy hotels and flying first class. A wardrobe full of designer clothes, shoes and handbags. A delightful little townhouse with a garden in a lovely area of London. A truly wonderful husband, and an active social life with lots of amazing friends and family. I had worked extremely hard to get where I was, but I felt very privileged to be living the life I was living.

But my priorities in life were changing. The travel and high-stress job were wearing me down. I wanted to spend more time with my new husband. I wanted a career that would be more flexible, more creative, more nurturing. I wanted a life that would enable me to have the children I had always wanted.

So, I started to tentatively explore ideas for my future. I had always loved food and anything health-related and enjoyed writing my own recipes. I decided to make this my creative outlet and started an Instagram account and blog. I learned a little about food photography and styling, loving being able to bring an artistic element into my life. It was a hobby, not a new career, but it was a positive step towards finding a new me.

At the same time, things were becoming increasingly challenging at work. The company I worked for (in fact, had been a founding member of), was struggling and changing direction. My role in its future wasn't as clear and I started to question more and more where my life was going. Then – BOOM. Cancer struck, and my entire world turned upside down.

It all began when I had a colonoscopy (that's a camera inserted into your bowels) after the irritable bowel symptoms I'd suffered from for years had become rather more serious and involved blood. It was meant to be routine – no one expected to find anything – but there in my colon was a polyp that had become a six-centimetre bleeding tumour.

I won't forget that moment, sitting in the hospital cubicle in my gown after the procedure, being told I might have cancer. I was 31 and in generally excellent health, so those words came as a huge shock. At the time I just cried, but this was in fact the real trigger I needed to turn my life around – in so many positive ways.

The following week my husband Brian and I went to Japan for a truly amazing holiday. We had to wait a couple of weeks for the biopsy test results, and this was a trip we'd planned for ages. Of course, there was a dark shadow cast by the wait, but we still had an incredible time, seeing the cherry blossom in full bloom (appropriately, a symbol of hope), eating amazing food and visiting temples galore.

When we returned it was to positive news. The biopsy showed only 'pre-cancerous' changes, so it was something that could be fixed by a straightforward operation to remove the offending mass. The operation was pretty unpleasant, but I didn't even have to stay in hospital overnight. That was it, my brush with cancer was all done and dusted. Or so we thought.

Of course, it wasn't that straightforward. Three months later when I had a follow-up, they found more polyps and, on cutting them out, managed to cause quite severe bleeding. It was an awful few days, but again, within a week I was out of hospital and 'cured'. I would need annual colonoscopies to check further polyps didn't develop, but otherwise, from a medical perspective, nothing.

However, the whole experience made me consider those questions that had started to niggle at me about where my life was going, and led me to make some very big changes. With my passion for food and health, nutrition seemed an obvious place to turn. I wanted to support my body as much as possible and do everything I could to keep myself in good health, so I started looking into nutrition courses for my own knowledge. But the more I looked, the more interested I became, until it started to dawn on me that this really could be a potential career.

The next few months were something of a blur of changes and big decisions. I had a new life plan in my head, and I was going for it! By October 2016, I'd left my City job and enrolled at the College of Naturopathic Medicine for a three-year course to qualify as a Nutritional Therapist. Then, to top it all off, I got pregnant. I really don't think for one moment that was a coincidence. Something in my body knew that I was making the changes to allow me to grow a baby. It was a momentous year to say the least, and I really felt I was answering the big questions about what I wanted from life.

———

I'm not going to pretend the next two years were all easy and rosy. I had a huge identity crisis when it hit that I no longer had a job. My career has always defined me and being 'just' a student was somehow really hard to take. I worried about not earning money, although was extremely fortunate to be able to live off my savings while I studied for three years. This is something for which I will be forever grateful and the reason I'll never regret my decade in high-stress City jobs, which enabled me to save well and have security. Still, it was weird going from being a high earner to earning nothing and I did worry about it at times.

> **"Pregnancy was a massive positive in my life. I felt amazing throughout the whole experience."**

Pregnancy was a massive positive in my life. I felt amazing throughout the whole experience. I was never sick or had any complaints. I loved my pregnant body and beautiful bump, felt incredibly blessed to be going through the experience of carrying a child and cherished every moment. I kept doing yoga until two weeks before the baby arrived, a practice that had always helped keep me grounded during times of stress at work, and I gave birth in a birthing pool to an incredible, healthy little boy, Oscar. He arrived the day before his due date, after 36 hours of labour and no pain relief – an indication of my insanely high pain threshold (which is now proving very useful!).

Come spring 2018, two years after the tumour was found, I had been through a lot of changes, making me really quite a different person. I was calmer, happier, fulfilled. I was a mum. I was studying something I found absolutely fascinating, I was picking up small amounts of paid work as a food blogger and photographer, which felt like a huge bonus on top of everything, and I looked and felt healthier than I'd ever been. I'd used my new nutritional knowledge to improve my diet and, as far as I could tell, I'd cured my irritable bowel syndrome. The bloating, diarrhoea and trapped wind I'd suffered for years had all disappeared.

It was fantastic. I was living the dream.

———

Things started to change in April 2018 when I woke up in the middle of the night as my back went 'pop'. I was in agonising pain but went to a chiropractor, who had me pain-free again in just a few days. Phew. Except then it happened again six weeks later, just before we were flying off on holiday. Back to the chiropractor, who luckily worked his magic, and other than a very uncomfortable flight out, my back was fine. We had a fabulous holiday relaxing on the white sandy beaches of the Seychelles (yup, really living the dream!). I even managed to fit in a couple of yoga classes on the beach.

But when we got home my back went again, and this time I was worried. The pain was unbelievable. I started to think that this was maybe more than just the wear and tear of carrying and breastfeeding a baby. After a couple of visits to my GP, I was referred to a physio, after which, with a lot of pushing on my part, I was referred for an MRI at the end of August. July and August were quite honestly hellish for me. I was often in so much pain that I couldn't leave the house. Lifting Oscar was impossible, and I had to cancel plan after plan. I was miserable.

So, the results of the MRI, while shocking, came with a certain relief knowing that I had an explanation for the pain. The MRI showed that one of my vertebrae had completely collapsed and there was a mass of tissue/inflammation pressing on the nerves (which had begun to cause a horrific numbness in my arm about a week before). My chiropractor took one look at the report the following day and told me to go straight to A&E.

The nightmare had begun.

I was admitted to The Royal London Hospital on 30th August 2018, where the testing began. Cancer was always a possibility, but in someone so young and otherwise healthy, it wasn't exactly top of the list. Instead there was a lot of focus on infectious diseases. Central London itself is something of a risk area, but I'd also travelled extensively and to some pretty remote and unusual places with my work, so it wasn't entirely impossible I'd picked up a strange disease.

After a large number of scans (CT/MRI/X-ray/ultrasound), endless blood tests and ten days on the Acute Assessment Ward, I finally had a spinal biopsy. That wasn't much fun. It was only under local anaesthetic, so I was awake, but had to stay completely still lying on my front. Not easy while in so much back pain. The doctor used a CT scanner, which I went in and out of multiple times, to guide the massive needle into my spine and get the tissue sample. The only thing that got me through it was knowing that this was the most likely thing to give us an answer to what was wrong.

A couple of days later, armed with a lot of painkillers, I was allowed home, as we knew the biopsy results could take a couple of weeks, maybe longer. It was so good to get out of hospital! Back to my boys (my husband Brian spent a lot of time in the hospital with me, but Oscar only visited a couple of times because hospitals and curious toddlers don't really mix, especially as Mummy was attached to all sorts of exciting looking machines!). I was also desperate to make my own food again. I'd had an amazing team of family and friends bringing me meals (Brian even made me a big superfood smoothie each morning), so I'd largely avoided hospital food, but being back in my own kitchen was still great.

It was our third wedding anniversary a couple of days later, and while we couldn't have a fancy meal out with champagne, we did have a lovely evening with some good food at home. In some ways the next couple of weeks were pretty normal. I needed help with Oscar as my back pain and increasing arm numbness meant I was limited, but friends and family stepped up and I was still very involved with everything around the house. I was even able to do little bits of work and photography.

The wait was hard, though. The painkillers helped, but I hated taking all the drugs. I was still in constant pain, and it already felt like I'd been through so much medically, yet not actually had any treatment. I also had to return to hospital for another scan, which showed a blood clot in my neck. This meant I had to inject myself daily with anticoagulants. Oh, another joy to add to the pile!

But the nightmare was about to take a turn for the worse.

On 18th September 2018, I went back to the Royal London for a follow-up about the blood clot. While I was there, I'd arranged to see the doctors for an update on my biopsy results. That's when we were given the news. The biopsy showed that the mass in my spine was a metastatic adenocarcinoma. In non-medical language, that meant it was cancer that had spread from somewhere else.

It may sound odd, but I actually felt some relief when I was told. *We had an answer!* The months of pain I'd endured would finally come to an end, because I'd be able to start treatment.

But of course, it wasn't quite so straightforward. They didn't know where the cancer had come from or where else it had spread, and until that was determined they couldn't treat me. More tests followed. First a PET scan, where you are injected with radioactive glucose that the cancer cells (and any other fast-growing cells) suck up, so they light up on a scan. The results of this weren't great. There were a lot of lit-up areas on my body; my spine, obviously, but also my lungs, liver, womb and pelvis, and patches on my thigh and neck. Seriously! How was I even functioning? I understood enough about PET scans to know that all of that might not necessarily be cancer, and so tried to stay positive that there were other explanations. In fact, the results on my womb were quickly ruled out as normal activity, which was a huge relief. I couldn't get my head around how this could have been a gynaecological cancer when I'd so recently had a healthy pregnancy and birth.

"I really don't think going over endless 'what if' scenarios is helpful, so I just tried to focus all my energy on the future . . ."

The areas on my lungs, pelvis and liver, however, looked strongly like cancer when matched to the CT scan, so I had to face the fact that I had stage IV cancer in at least four places in my body. As the days ticked on, I became more and more fearful that I was going to be officially diagnosed with Cancer of an Unknown Primary. The problem with such cancers (which actually make up around 3 per cent of diagnoses) is that it is hard to make treatment very targeted. For me, it also made it impossible to get my head around *why* I had cancer, a question that must be on the forefront of every cancer patient's mind.

Luckily though, ten days later we got (what I considered) good news. We met the oncologists at St Bartholomew's Hospital and the doctor told us results had come in that day that were strongly suggestive of bowel cancer. I almost cried with joy! I know it sounds odd, but this was actually an answer, and one that made a certain amount of sense to me. Of course it made us immediately start to question the previous diagnosis and why wider tests hadn't been done two years before – but I really don't think going over endless 'what if' scenarios is helpful, so I just tried to focus all my energy on the future and what we could do now. The interesting thing was that the scans didn't show up anything particular in my colon. Had it been removed during my surgery two years ago? Was the original tumour so small that they couldn't see it? Or had my dietary and lifestyle changes, and the gut clearing protocol I'd followed for my IBS, actually got rid of the original cancer? We'll probably never know, but I got some comfort from the fact that it wasn't all over my bowels, and felt I must already be doing some things right.

However, the pressing issue remained my back. In fact, the week before we'd met the neurosurgery team at the Royal London Hospital, who'd fitted me with a fetching back brace (Oscar thought this was hilarious, his very own robot mum with buttons). They wanted to operate to stabilise the spine where the tumour had caused the collapse, and hopefully prevent any more nerve damage where it was compressing the nerves to my arms and hands. As long as the oncology team were prepared to delay treatment until I was recovered, spinal surgery was planned for 3rd October. The oncology team were fully supportive of this as a first step. While I specifically asked not to be given a length of life/ chance of survival prognosis, I did ask them to tell me if they thought I only had a matter of weeks to live, in which case I may have acted differently. Luckily, they confirmed that this was not the situation, and felt that, from what we knew, the cancer was not so fast-growing that we couldn't hold off on starting treatment until we had stabilised my back.

So, treatment began.

> **"There was already a silver lining to my illness, as friends and family stepped up to help out and offer support beyond anything I could have imagined."**

While I knew the spinal surgery was a serious operation, at this point I didn't feel I had any choice. My right-hand function was deteriorating by the day, which was making even the simplest day-to-day activities hard and made being alone with Oscar completely out of the question. I was on lots of painkillers and steroids to control the inflammation around the tumour, and the side effects were starting to show; grogginess and horrific acne being the two that were really starting to get me down.

I have to say here, I'd never realised what an incredible support network I had around me until cancer came along. There was already a silver lining to my illness, as friends and family stepped up to help out and offer support beyond anything I could have imagined. Between them, my amazing parents and Brian's wonderful mum were taking it in turns to live with us to help out. Sure, all being under one roof came with its own challenges, but I will be eternally grateful for their help, and it was impressive how we all settled into our roles in this weird new routine. Oscar, quite frankly, was having a ball, with his grandparents and uncle and aunt showering him with extra love and attention. I saw friends who I'd not seen in ages, even reconnecting with my best friend from university who I'd pretty much lost touch with ten years before. Two of my closest friends, both pregnant, visited me time and again, and chatting baby stuff was such a joy, making me even more determined to get through the cancer. I also found huge support from my blog and social media followers. I'd decided being open was the best option as I didn't want to hide away from the world. Sharing the news was such a good move, enabling me to continue posting when I felt like it, but with plenty of support and understanding when I couldn't.

Anyway, back to the surgery. I was readmitted to the Royal London Hospital on 3rd October (I really should have a gold loyalty card by now…), ready to be operated on by Mr Bull (who'd amusingly made bull horn gestures with his hands when he'd introduced himself the week before, but who we'd researched and realised was a top guy in his game). He'd explained that his aim was to stabilise my spine by inserting metal pins, but he wouldn't be removing the tumour as this carried too great a risk of causing permanent nerve damage. That felt kind of weird, but I understood the reasoning and felt that it was right to let the expert do what he felt was best.

The day didn't start brilliantly as I passed out while the nurse was doing all the pre-admission checks. I'd not been allowed to eat that morning and I really am a disaster if I don't have breakfast! Anyway, I recovered quickly and luckily was the first patient on the list, so there was very little waiting around. I remember being wheeled into pre-theatre and breathing into an oxygen mask as the clock in front ticked to 9 a.m. The next thing I knew, I was coming round in the recovery ward, and it was apparently 3 p.m. The first thing I did was wriggle my fingers and toes. *Yay!* They worked – I hadn't been paralysed (a small but pretty significant risk of the surgery). Then I asked for Brian, who was luckily brought in very shortly afterwards as he had been charming his way past all the staff (he shouldn't really have been in the recovery ward!). Guess what his first question was? 'Can you wriggle your toes?' The poor guy had had it way worse than me that day, anxiously waiting to hear if all had gone to plan.

Much to our surprise, I didn't feel too awful and even wanted to eat, although Brian did have to spoon-feed me like a baby as I could barely move. To be honest, compared to many of the things he's had to do since, that was nothing. Thank goodness he's so awesome, and all this is only making us stronger. He stayed as long as he could while I waited to be moved to a ward, but he was kicked out in the evening. A little later I was moved to an intensive monitoring neurosurgery ward… me and three old men, brilliant! I was so drugged up I did manage a little sleep, but when I woke up in the morning, everything started to hit me.

A happy, healthy you

I was wired up in every way possible, from painkillers on a drip, to a blood pressure cuff that squeezed me on the hour, to a catheter doing, well, its thing, and numerous other devices I can't even remember. I couldn't work out how much pain I was in from surgery and how much was discomfort from all the monitoring. I was desperate to start getting back to normal, but when I tried to sit up, I passed out. Twice. Apparently, that was completely normal, but I can't lie, I felt pretty demoralised.

But things improved over the course of the day. I used my best charm to beg the nurses to find me a private side room, which they did, and that evening I even managed to get out of bed. The following day I was much more mobile, although as the drugs started to wear off, I got a feel for the real post-surgery pain… eek! On the plus side, I realised I could lie on my side, something I hadn't been able to do for months due to my back pain, so the surgery had clearly helped with the stabilisation. Not so positive was my hand function, which actually felt worse. Of course, there was going to be a lot of inflammation from the surgery, and nerve compression isn't something that is solved quickly, but this did worry and upset me.

I had a scan to check that the 12 titanium pins they had inserted were still all in the right places. They were, and, as I was able to get out of bed and my vitals were all stable, the neurosurgeons said I could go home on day three. We were in shock. I'd expected to be in hospital for at least a week. But home was definitely preferable, and by that evening, after one pretty excruciating taxi journey, I was back in my own bed, with my family around me.

——

So far, I'd viewed my cancer as something I needed to get through and put behind me, although I was aware that with stage IV cancer, there would always be the risk of recurrence. However, this changed when I saw my oncologist post-surgery and he broke the news to us that my cancer was considered incurable. While there was treatment I could have, it would be palliative (which means reducing side effects and attempting to lengthen life). They didn't believe they would ever be able to rid me of cancer.

His words were a shock and the tears flowed. The enormity of the situation hit home more than it had done so far, and I had an increasing awareness that my life was never fully going to go back to normal, or at least not to how I'd planned. But I took the view that I had to face this like I'd faced everything else on this journey: head on, refusing to be beaten. I felt like cancer and I were having a fight.

Cancer: Punch in the back – ouch, bad back.

Me: Punch back, no big deal, a bad back's not stopping me.

Cancer: Punch in the back number two – collapsed vertebra.

Me: Punch back. This is totally fixable, bring on surgery.

Cancer: Third punch in the back – it's a tumour.

Me: Head high, punch back again – screw you cancer, tumours can be annihilated.

Cancer (getting mean): Punch in the liver, lungs, couple of lymph nodes too – widespread stage IV cancer.

Me: Punch back – ha to stage IV, still totally treatable.

Cancer: Big punch – actually nope, incurable.

Me: Heavy crash to the floor… But wait, I'm not done yet, cancer. See, I'm getting up and brushing myself off. A bit bruised (literally, thanks to all the needles and tubes that have been stuck into me recently) and tired, but I am oh-so-ready for the next round and I'm bringing in my army. Meet radiotherapy, chemotherapy, the best nutritional help I can get, and a massive desire to live!

Yes team, I was ready for this. No prognosis would take away my hope, strength and positivity. I love my life and my family and friends way too much to even vaguely begin to give up. And actually, when I rationalised things, incurable didn't have to change anything I was doing. It sounded scary but, in fact, with what I'd learned, both in college and in the mountains of cancer literature I was reading, I had started to understand how sometimes it is possible to live with cancer and manage it like any other chronic disease. There are many incredible, inspiring stories of people out there who are doing just that. Sure, it would mean some lifestyle changes, but many of those I had already made, and I loved healthy living. Honestly, I'd choose a salad over a takeaway any day! And other things I'd just get used to. Staying alive is a big incentive for pretty much anything, I can tell you.

My initial treatment plan was explained to me: first radiotherapy (targeted X-rays) on my spine to shrink the tumour that was still causing nerve compression; then chemotherapy drugs (indefinitely) to hopefully stop any further spread, and maybe even shrink the existing tumours if we were lucky. I was very weak post-surgery and had lost nearly 20 per cent of my body weight (and I was slim to start with), so I had to start preparing myself mentally and physically for this gruelling treatment regime.

I started daily meditation and gratitude practice, making sure I found something to be positive about every day, however small, and however rubbish I was feeling. I started to prioritise taking a few special minutes just for me each day. After all, being a mum to a toddler is pretty all-consuming, even with family helping out! Meditation was something I had been meaning to do for so long and never prioritised, but now it's something without which my day wouldn't feel complete. Giving myself that time has enabled me to see more clearly the positives in my life. Be it the big ones, like my incredible family, or the small ones, like the joy I feel sitting in my little garden that I've nurtured for years.

On the physical side, I did everything I could to prepare and protect my body for and from the drugs, using complementary medicine and living as healthily as possible. Recovering from surgery made this tough in some ways. Ideally, I would have been getting plenty of exercise, oxygenating my body (cancer cells thrive in an anaerobic environment, i.e. they hate oxygen), but at this point even deep breathing and gentle stretching was painful. What I did do was focus on what I put into my body in terms of food and some special supplements. I already had my diet pretty well covered, but I started working with a nutritional therapist and functional medicine doctor who specialises in supporting cancer patients. She gave me a few extra pointers on diet and introduced a supplement protocol to help boost my immune system, support blood circulation (getting the oxygen that cancer hates around my body as effectively as possible) and support the apoptosis of the cancer cells (apoptosis is the body's way of killing off bad cells, but it doesn't occur properly with cancer).

It wasn't easy, and of course there were changes I had to make to my life, but increasingly I was reaching a place where I was at peace with the fact that I was living with cancer, potentially had been for a little while in fact, and hoped I could continue to do so for a long time to come.

My cancer treatment started with radiotherapy, which is essentially very strong X-rays that are used to nuke (non-technical term) tumours. It is very targeted, which means that the side effects generally aren't too bad (although that does depend on the length of treatment and where you have it). Radiotherapy is generally done over a series of days or weeks, on a daily basis until enough radiation has been given to shrink the tumour as far as possible whilst doing minimal damage to healthy surrounding tissue.

"I found something to be positive about every day, however small, and however rubbish I was feeling."

I was very positive about starting with this treatment as, while the bigger picture was rather overwhelming at times, having an end goal of fixing the issues of my back pain and hand function was a great thing to focus on.

The treatment began with a 'planning' session where they prepped me by tattooing me! As the treatment is so targeted, it is crucial that they aim the radiation at exactly the right place. I lay on a scanner and was measured in about a million different ways so they would know where to put me and how to set everything up for each treatment. The tattoo was a tiny dot to act as a final accuracy point for them to line up. I knew it was coming and it hadn't bothered me at all, but I'd just assumed that I would be lying on my front and that the dot would be on my back, as that's where the radiation was going. But no… actually I was lying on my back, so the tattoo was done on my front. I know it sounds silly in the grand scheme of things, but I cried when it was done. I think it was that feeling of losing control, as it wasn't what I'd expected. I felt like a massive idiot, but the radiographer was so sweet and gave me a hug.

The actual treatment started a few days later. I just had a short course over five days (daily, with a break over the weekend). Each day, I lay on a bed and was measured all over to get everything just right. It felt a bit like being part of a NASA experiment or something (probably helped by the fact that the radiotherapy rooms at St Bart's are all named after planets… I had a day in Saturn, two in Jupiter and two in Mercury). The radiotherapy itself was extremely quick (a few minutes) and totally painless – just like having an X-ray. Easy!

However, the way radiotherapy works is that, in killing off the tumour cells, it inflames everything in the area. I'd been warned this would happen and that my pain was likely to increase, more and more each day, but I *massively* underestimated this on day one. I was in agony afterwards. My poor husband and parents who were staying with us to help with Oscar had the full force of a *very* grumpy Caroline that evening! Next day I upped my pain meds (which, to be fair, I'd been told I'd probably need to do) and days two and three weren't nearly so bad. Unfortunately, over the weekend, the radiotherapy continued to increase inflammation and my hand function deteriorated significantly, which was so frustrating. It felt like a huge step backwards in my surgery recovery, but I knew I just had to be patient and wait for the inflammation to subside. My lack of hand function was the thing I found hardest, though, as I was completely dependent on others to do a million little things for me. I'm such an independent person and rubbish at asking for help at any time.

The next stage in my treatment was chemotherapy, which is treatment for cancer using drugs. There are many different chemotherapy drugs available; some are given intravenously (into the blood) and some orally, as tablets. While chemotherapy is becoming increasingly sophisticated and targeted, most forms do, unfortunately, kill off some good cells as well as cancer cells (especially ones that, like cancer cells, have a fast turnover), which means it can have some fairly unpleasant side effects. Chemotherapy can be given for any time period, from ongoing daily tablets to a set number of intravenous cycles (generally 14 or 21 days), where the drugs are given at the beginning of the cycle, with a break until the next cycle.

I was rather dreading starting chemotherapy. The difficulty is that each individual responds differently, so until you've started, you don't know how you will feel, or whether the treatment will work. My fear was that I would feel horrendous for three months before we even knew if it was doing any good. So, I was pleasantly surprised by how my first cycle went.

I was initially given FOLFIRI, which is a combination of chemotherapy drugs used for a number of different cancers, given intravenously. It is given on a 14-day cycle that goes like this: on day one, I'd see my oncologist and have my bloods taken to make sure I was well enough to have chemotherapy. Day two, I'd spend on the chemotherapy ward having a number of drugs administered via a drip (which took about five hours), then I'd go home with a pump attached to me that continued to drip in the final drug for another two days. On day four the pump would be disconnected, and I'd have a break for 10 days until the next cycle began. The side effects can last for up to 10 days… So basically, the whole time!

Determined to go into the treatment with as much positivity as possible, I loaded up the iPad with chick flicks and put on my best red lipstick (I wanted to wear killer heels, too, but it'd been so long since I'd worn a pair that I was worried I'd fall off them, and I didn't think my neurosurgeon would be too happy about that…). I'd already seen one of the wards so knew roughly what to expect, and my oncologist had explained the process and drugs I would receive, so I was fairly relaxed about it all. There is always a risk of having a reaction to one of the drugs, especially the first time, but I knew the nurses would be monitoring me closely.

> "Determined to go into the treatment with as much positivity as possible, I loaded up the iPad with chick flicks and put on my best red lipstick."

There isn't a huge amount to say about the rest of the day because it was very uneventful. I felt a little dizzy and my vision blurred with the first chemotherapy drug, but the doctor assured me this was a known side effect and it didn't last long. Five hours sitting in a chair is rather dull, but I watched a couple of films, had some lunch (avoiding hospital food as usual), and then I was done. My pump was attached and home I went (with a plan to buy a glittery bag to hold the pump in future). The pump looked like a water bottle with a balloon inside that slowly deflated, pushing the drug into my bloodstream. It was a little awkward, but not painful, and it wasn't as bad to sleep with as I thought it might be.

So far so good, but I was bracing myself for side effects. Chemotherapy has various systemic side effects including lowering your immune system, making you very susceptible to illness and infection. This is something I'll always have to be aware of. (It's not easy to keep clear of germs living in central London and with a small child, but I do my best!) For my drugs, the common side effects were also nausea and gut upsets, fatigue, sensitive skin (especially sore hands and feet), hair thinning or loss and mouth ulcers. All fun stuff. While on the pump I had a mildly upset gut and felt fairly tired by the third day. And that was it! A couple of days later I felt normal again, and as my back pain was easing and my hand function was (very slowly) improving, I felt better than I had for quite a while. While I knew that the effects were likely to increase with each cycle, it was a huge relief that the first one went well and I felt far more comfortable about being able to face this phase of my challenge.

———

When I started chemotherapy in November 2018, I had a baseline CT scan which the doctors would then be able to compare to another scan done after three months of treatment to determine whether the chemotherapy was working. As I also had a CT scan when I was first admitted to hospital at the end of August, they were able to compare the two to see how the cancer was progressing.

While I really hoped that the scan would show no progression in the cancer, I knew this was unlikely, so I was disappointed but not exactly surprised when I was told the tumours on my lungs, liver and various lymph nodes had grown in size. On the plus side, there was still nothing in my colon. While I will never give up hope, I have to be honest – the cancer progression did give me a reality check on my chances of long-term survival.

> **"While I will never give up hope, I have to be honest – the cancer progression did give me a reality check on my chances of long-term survival."**

Given the progression, and now that we had a little more idea of how aggressive the cancer was and how I was coping with chemotherapy, my oncologist and I talked further about the treatment options. We discussed the various newer treatments, like CyberKnife treatment, but unfortunately my cancer is too widespread for this to be of any use. At this point, by far the best option remained chemotherapy, which would hopefully stop the cancer growing for a while. There were two drug combinations that were first line treatment options for me: FOLFIRI and FOLFOX. I was given FOLFIRI. However, given the cancer's progression and because I'd tolerated the first round of chemotherapy so well, my oncologist suggested adding in Oxaliplatin on top of the FOLFIRI (FOLFOXIRI!). A recent trial where the drugs were combined had shown that those who had all of them from the start of chemotherapy had a prolonged period of stability before the cancer returned to progression compared with those on one or the other. While this might make the chemotherapy side effects tougher, I was prepared to give anything a go to give myself the best chance of living longer.

Chemotherapy did get harder, with more fatigue, a loss of appetite, occasional nausea and a horrid taste in my mouth, hideous mouth ulcers after some rounds and peripheral neuropathy (painful prickling in my fingers and toes, and mild spasms of my lips) when exposed to the cold.

In February 2019, I had the three month chemotherapy CT scan. After a fairly agonising week of waiting, we saw my oncologist on an unseasonably sunny morning (a great start), made infinitely better when he greeted us with the words, 'The scan is good!'. It seemed the chemotherapy (and hopefully all of the complementary things I'd been doing) had been working well and most of the tumours had actually shrunk. This was the best possible outcome – even no growth would have been a cause for celebration, but shrinkage was fantastic. Of course, it didn't change the fact that I had tumours in multiple places (liver, lungs, peritoneum, spine), which means I was in no way operable (i.e. incurable, so potentially on chemotherapy for life), and one of the liver tumours looked slightly larger, which was a little concerning, but the fact that chemotherapy was at least largely working bought us *time*, and time, when you have a terminal illness, is the most you can ask for.

—

Sadly, the news since that first scan has not been good and cancer has continued to throw challenge after challenge at me. The next scan, in May, showed the cancer was growing, with new lesions on my liver, and scans in August and October were similar. I have had fluid build-up round my heart and in my lungs, which resulted in A&E admissions and an operation to cut a hole in the sac surrounding my heart to allow fluid to drain off. I've had various chemotherapy drugs and a targeted drug called Herceptin, as we know I have a particular mutation (HER2+) that it aims to correct. Sadly, none of these to date have worked on my liver tumours, and I am fast running out of options.

There are no obvious further treatments available at the moment (although I continue with chemotherapy to try to slow the growth as much as possible), and I know my prognosis is now very poor. I don't know how long I have left on this earth and I have to just take one day at a time. Having cancer is tough, the treatment is tough, and many days are a struggle, but every day I do my best to feel happy, grateful and positive. I have learned to plan in short-term, bite-sized chunks of time, and, bit by bit, I keep building on my 'new normal'. I am, in many ways, able to live a happy and healthy life; spending time with my precious family, eating well, practising mindfulness and doing yoga. Right now, I am glad for the life I have, and will continue doing all I can to stay positive and make it as long a life as possible.

—

Caroline died on 22 January 2020 surrounded by her loved ones. Caroline would have loved to know that you are reading this book and that her memory is preserved through these recipes. As you are adding some turmeric or ginger, please smile and think of her.

'Fall in love
with taking care
of yourself'

– Sylvester Mcnutt

Part one:

A healthy you begins with
a healthy mind

Are you happy with your life? The big questions

When my original tumour was discovered, I was given a real wake-up call. Was I living the life I really wanted to live? I sat down and asked myself the four questions below, and I'd encourage all of you to do the same, right now; don't wait for a big event or pivotal moment to stop and think about where your life is going. These are simple yet very powerful questions that will help you to take stock and get perspective on your life and what makes you happy.

- What do I want from life?
- What makes me happy?
- What makes me unhappy?
- What changes can I make?

You may have lots of little answers to each question, or maybe there will be certain things that leap out as overall themes. For me, they were family and creativity; two things I knew that I wanted more of in my life that were currently lacking. And so, starting with these big-picture ideas, I was able to start to formulate a plan to make my dream life a reality.

Another little exercise is to imagine your ideal life in the future, say five to ten years down the line, then think about what changes you can make to bring those dreams to life right now! Sure, some things may need to wait, but if your dream is to live by the sea, why not move to the sea? We all put up barriers to things we think aren't possible, or are too complicated or challenging, but if you really want something, so often you can find a way.

For me, thinking about my ideal life was a very calming exercise, as now there isn't a huge amount that I want to be different. Because of the changes I had already made since leaving my City job and having Oscar, I have the family I really wanted and the new, more flexible and creative career, but a couple of years before that this would have been exactly the right exercise for me, and others may gain a lot from it. It's all too easy to put things off for 'the future', but if I have one overarching piece of advice, it is this: don't wait for tomorrow to make changes in your life that will bring you joy; don't put off doing what you really want to do in life. Reach for your dreams right now. You may amaze yourself by how far you can go. None of us know what is around the corner, so sit down today and think about how you can make your life better.

A happy, healthy you

See the positive in every day

I will never be glad to have cancer. It has put me and those close to me through a lot of misery, and I know there will be plenty more tough times to come. But a diagnosis like this really does help you live in the moment and find the positive in every day. People frequently tell me that I'm so strong for keeping going, or that if it were them in my position, they wouldn't get out of bed. I don't think either of these things are true. Yes, I am strong, but I don't need strength to get up and enjoy life each day. Life is a blessing. Each morning I wake up grateful that I'm alive. I want to get up, go out, enjoy myself. Even when I have to deal with pain, even if I feel very tired, I know that the day will bring some joy, so it is worth embracing. Perhaps there will be a beautiful blue sky overhead, perhaps Oscar will say something particularly funny or cute, perhaps I'll have a lovely phone call with a friend, or a tasty dinner with Brian. All small things that bring me joy and make me grateful for each day.

We all have things to be grateful for, so when you've read this, spend a few minutes thinking about what they are. They may be big things such as family, your health, a home, a job, or small things like those I listed above. You may like to keep a gratitude journal, writing down each day something you have been grateful for. Or just spend two minutes before you go to bed thinking of something that has made you smile that day. It may well make you feel calmer and help with sleep, too, as you end the day thinking positive thoughts, not worrying about the million and one little things that didn't go so well, or that you need to do tomorrow.

If you have children, perhaps ask everyone to say something they have been grateful for or enjoyed that day as you sit down for dinner. Even though Oscar is only two, I like to ask him each evening what he enjoyed about his day, and what made him happy. I think that getting into the habit of thinking in such a way is very powerful.

It's okay to have down days

While I believe 100 per cent in seeing the positive in every day, I also think it's important to accept that it's not possible to feel positive all of the time – after all, we're only human. I've certainly had some big wobbles, and if you are reading this going through cancer or any other tough situation, know that wobbles are completely allowed! A good cry is incredibly cathartic.

I've cried over the small things and big things; not being able to tie up my own hair due to the weakness of my hand, not being able to cuddle my son better when he cries, and on many occasions, over how fed up I am of not being able to live my life normally. But crying about these things is a release and afterwards I feel calmer and able to think about the positives in my life.

When you are finding things particularly tough, I think the important thing is to recognise the negative emotions, then try to understand *why* you are feeling them. Once you've done that, you are much better placed to work out how to take control of them and stop them from taking over and pushing you into a negative spiral.

Since being diagnosed with cancer, the biggest negative emotion for me hasn't been sadness or fear or anger (although all have been present from time to time), but frustration. From reading my story, you'll probably realise that I am very independent and like to be in control and, if cancer has done one thing, it's taken away so much of the control I had over my life. While I have used my drive and independence as a strength in many ways, enabling me to achieve a lot and have a successful career, when I feel out of control, I struggle.

Let me share a little story that is a classic example. Before my chemotherapy began, I went to the hospital to have a PICC line inserted. This is a permanent 'access point' to my veins for my chemotherapy drugs to be pumped into each cycle, and it is something I'd rather been dreading. It just sounded a miserable procedure, I wasn't looking forward to having this thing in my arm for the foreseeable future, and it made chemotherapy, which I was *really* not looking forward to, a reality. But I'd psyched myself up and was ready for the procedure. So off I went to hospital with my mum (in unbelievably poor timing, Brian had started a new job that week so was rather busy).

We went up to the chemotherapy unit at St Bart's, the first time I'd been there. Oh my, it was depressing. A waiting room full of sad, ill-looking people, the youngest of whom was probably close to twice my age. It was a reality check moment… this was now my life. I'd be spending one day a fortnight here for the indefinite future.

Trying to push these thoughts to the back of my mind, I followed the nurse through to the room where she was going to insert my line. But when we discussed which of my arms she was going to put it in, and I pointed out that I had a blood clot in the left side of my neck, it turned out there was a problem, as no one seemed to have taken this into account. After a few phone calls I was told I'd need a portacath, which is put under the skin on the chest, instead of a PICC in my arm. This was a bigger procedure, so wouldn't be possible to do until the following week. I was so frustrated! Why had no one thought about this before? What a wasted journey into hospital (I was still in pain and tired as I was recovering from the double whammy of surgery and radiotherapy, so even getting to hospital was quite an undertaking for me). I went home feeling so fed up, and I'm ashamed to admit that I lost it that evening. The reality of the foreseeable future, combined with things not going to plan and making me feel out of control and deeply frustrated, was all just too much.

While I could most definitely have dealt with the situation better, actually having a good cry and a bit of a shout and scream was what I needed. Sometimes it's helpful to give yourself a release and allow the negative emotions some space rather than always bottling them up. And once I'd let the feelings out, I was able to calmly look at the positives of the situation instead and regain a feeling of control. Actually, a portacath was probably a better option than a PICC; while more serious to insert and remove, once in, it is less noticeable than a PICC and easier to look after. And delaying chemotherapy a week wasn't all bad either. Of course, we wanted to start whacking the cancer ASAP, but chemotherapy takes a big toll on the body, so having another week to recover from surgery and radiotherapy and build up my strength was a good thing.

So, a little lesson to share from this story – it's okay to have a down day, but regardless of whether you're dealing with something like a serious illness, or simply the stresses and strains of everyday life, next time negative emotions get on top of you, try the following: Recognise the emotion and let it out. Maybe you want to cry or shout, or maybe you can even channel that negativity into exercise, like hitting a punch bag!

Try to understand why you felt that emotion, and especially what triggered it. When you've given yourself a chance to release the emotion, try to find a positive in the situation or a way to turn around whatever the trigger was. Sometimes this won't be easy, but often just the process of stopping and thinking about the situation can help prevent a downward spiral of negative emotion.

Take time for you and learn to love and care for your body and mind

We all lead such fast-paced and busy lives in this age of technology and digital connection. Often, we don't take the time to listen to our bodies and relax. But it's so important to nourish and care for both your body and mind.

Here are my top tips:
- Don't ever feel guilty for taking time for you. You will be a better partner, parent, friend or employee if you are healthy and happy.
- Set aside a special time for yourself each day, whether that is 10 minutes of mindfulness each morning or a bath before bed; make that time precious and your own.
- Fall in love with taking care of yourself. Too often, self-care and making the healthy choice can seem like too much effort or a chore, but they shouldn't be. If you don't enjoy doing these things, you won't do them, certainly not in the long term. So, find healthy options and actions of self-care that you do want to choose, and they'll be much easier to implement into your daily life.
- Do something today that your future self will thank you for; give your body and mind a break from time to time, eat well, sleep well, and go to the doctor with any concerns you've been putting off addressing.
- Treat your health as an investment, not an expense. If you think being healthy is costly, try being ill – it's far more expensive, believe me! So, spend both the time and money you can on looking after yourself, whether that involves buying good-quality food and doing home cooking, seeing a nutritionist or other therapist, or treating yourself to a little holiday!

A healthy lifestyle

There are three key lifestyle factors whose management is essential for good mental as well as physical health. Each could demand a book in its own right (and indeed there are many good books available on all of these topics), but managing each one properly is so fundamental to good health that I feel I must touch on them:
- Movement
- Sleep
- Stress

Movement

This section is called 'movement', rather than 'exercise' because it is moving your body that is important. The term 'exercise' tends to conjure up images of running or the gym or other hard physical activities, which, although very beneficial in their own right, are only a subset of the many ways you can get movement into your life.

Countless research has found movement beneficial physically and mentally, both for those who are generally healthy, and those suffering from chronic illness, including those being treated for cancer. Movement is good for the whole body, from the bones, muscles and joints (keeping everything strong and flexible), to the heart and rest of the cardiovascular system, as well as the lungs and the brain.

So, try to move your body every day. Perhaps you do enjoy exercise; running, swimming, cycling, gym work, or something gentler like yoga or tai chi. Perhaps movement comes as part of a social life; dancing with friends or going for a country walk (to the pub!). Or perhaps a wander round the garden or the park with a few gentle stretches is your limit. That's absolutely fine too. Just make sure you do something every day, and do something you enjoy so it isn't a chore. Try to integrate movement into your daily routine. For example, walk part of your way to work, do a mini workout or some stretches as the dinner cooks (this can be fun to do if you have children too – make it a family activity!). YouTube is a treasure trove of home workouts and ideas, so you don't need to have a gym membership or any fancy equipment to get your body moving.

Sleep

Sleep is the body's recovery time. It is absolutely vital that we all get enough. Certainly, some people seem to manage well on far less sleep than others, but a lack of sleep has long-term impacts on the hormone (endocrine) system, can increase chronic inflammation, impact on mood and concentration, and even result in weight gain. There have been many highly regarded scientific papers on the importance of sleep, but it's something people underestimate again and again.

When we sleep, the body undertakes various growth, repair and regeneration processes (which is why children, who are growing, need significantly more sleep than adults). Hormones are released that regulate appetite, growth and stress; the immune system has a chance to strengthen and repair; and the brain goes through various processes including memory consolidation.

A happy, healthy you

But getting good-quality sleep isn't always easy. These are my top tips on implementing good sleep hygiene into your life, to maximise those hours under the covers!

- Try to be consistent in when you sleep, and how long for. You want to support your body's natural circadian rhythm, so going to bed and getting up at around the same time each day is important.
- Aim for 7–8 hours' sleep a night. Yes, many people get used to living with less, but research has shown that for optimal health, pretty much all adults need this amount.
- Sleep in a room that is as dark as possible (this helps with melatonin production, a key hormone required for sleep), and make sure it is not too hot.
- Avoid screens for at least an hour before bed. They emit blue light, which interferes with the circadian rhythm. If you really need to use screens late in the evening, try wearing blue-light-blocking glasses, and switching your phone to night mode (where the screen goes a little orange and emits less blue light).
- Don't eat too close to bedtime. Ideally, you want to have at least two hours for your food to start digesting before going to sleep.
- People have different sensitivities to caffeine, but it is best to avoid caffeinated drinks from late afternoon onwards. Chamomile and lavender teas are excellent calming drinks for the evening.
- Other stimulants, including alcohol and tobacco, are also known sleep disruptors.
- Certain foods can increase melatonin, tart cherries being the most well-known. You can buy Montmorency cherry juice or supplements in health food stores.
- Try an Epsom salt bath for relaxation. The salts are a form of magnesium, which is important for muscle and nerve relaxation. Add a drop of lavender bath oil for extra sleep-inducing bliss!

Stress

Stress has an enormous impact on both physical and mental health, and unfortunately, very few people are able to avoid it completely. Instead we have to learn to manage it, and ensure we have ways to reduce stress when it gets too much.

I want to explain a little of the science behind stress and the nervous system, as learning these basics really gave me an enormous appreciation of the impact stress has on us physically as well as mentally.

Our nervous system is made up of the Parasympathetic Nervous System (PNS) and Sympathetic Nervous System (SNS). The SNS is known as the 'flight or fight' response, while the PNS is all about 'rest and digest'. The SNS is what responds to stress; it is vital for our existence, as it gives us the 'get up and go' to get out of bed in the morning. It pumps out adrenaline when we need it and prepares the body for action. The PNS, on the other hand, acts when we are resting. It enables food to be digested, body tissues to grow and repair, and the reproductive system to work.

These two systems work very much in balance, to the extent that, when one is working hard, the other has a break (all very unscientifically put, but I want to make it simple to understand!). You can almost think of it like a pair of weighing scales: PNS up, SNS down, and vice versa.

This makes sense when you think about it. The SNS, fight or flight, kicks in when we need an adrenaline rush. For ancient man, this may have been when a wild animal was chasing him. At times like this, the body needs to put all resources into being able to run fast. The heart beats harder, blood vessels dilate, muscles kick into action. There is no energy left to be digesting food, or repairing the body.

And this is all fine, unless the SNS is switched on too much. And this is what happens when we are continually, or chronically, stressed. You might not be running from a lion, but you may well have a boss breathing down your neck, a hundred deadlines to meet, the supermarket shop to do, dinner to make, children to pick up from school… and all these things can put your body into a state of chronic stress. This means the PNS struggles to get a look in. There is no time for your body to recover and repair (which it must do on an ongoing basis), and no time for your digestive system to work properly.

Ever noticed that you go down with colds easily or get a dodgy belly when you are stressed? It's because the SNS/PNS balance is tipped too much towards SNS. I used to get my worst irritable bowel flare-ups when I was stressed at work. Stress was a much bigger driver than any food trigger, and when I learned about the nervous system, I understood why!

So, think about how you can reduce stress so that your SNS isn't overworked, and your PNS is supported. Managing stress is very different for everyone, but top researched methods include the following:

- Exercise. More about this below, but getting active is a brilliant way to help manage stress. Even something high intensity can help you channel stress into something positive, and will mean dopamine, our feel-good hormone, is released.
- Meditation. This doesn't have to mean sitting cross-legged on the floor humming! Just taking time to be quiet and reflective can help your whole body slow down. There are some superb resources and apps, such as Headspace and Calm, which can get you started on learning to meditate. I used these a lot when first diagnosed and they have given me an excellent set of tools to use whenever I feel stress building up.
- Yoga. Essentially a combination of exercise and meditation, yoga offers a double benefit for managing stress. It can help relax and slow you down physically and mentally, and ground you in the moment.
- Breathing. A little like a form of meditation, and often used in yoga, there are many breathing exercises that can act as a natural tranquiliser of the nervous system. Try a technique called 4–7 breathing:
  - Exhale through your mouth.
  - Inhale through your nose for a count of four.
  - Pause.
  - Exhale through your mouth for a count of seven.
  - Repeat three times.

Everyone has their own ways of relaxing and de-stressing, so find something that works for you; maybe you like having long baths, listening to music, doing something creative or getting outside. There is no right or wrong; the important point is to learn to become mindful and aware of when and why you are stressed, and do your best to reduce this stress in any way you can.

'Healthy isn't

a goal, it's a

way of living'

Part two:

A healthy home
and environment

In the world we live in, it is impossible to avoid all toxins and stresses. We are surrounded by them. From traffic pollution to chemicals in our toiletries, there are many sources of free radicals that cause damage to the body. However, there are a few things we can all do to limit our exposure to these, and make our homes as healthy as possible.

Light

Exposing yourself to natural light is incredibly important to ensure your circadian rhythm is working. This is the wake/sleep cycle and it enables you to have most energy during the day and sleep well at night. Unfortunately, as we are constantly exposed to unnatural light forms, and spend huge amounts of time indoors, our circadian rhythm can easily get out of balance. Here are a few things you can do to help it get back on track:

Get outside as much as possible during the day, especially in the morning when you want your body to get into 'wake-up' mode. Avoid wearing sunglasses in the morning if possible, as these make your brain think it's darker and later than it actually is. Try simple things like taking a five-minute stroll round your garden before breakfast, getting off the bus a stop early or parking your car a little further from the office, to have a short walk first thing.

Sit by a window whenever possible and maximise natural light in your home or office. Keep windows clean and uncovered where you can.

If you are in a dark environment a lot during the day, try a natural light lamp/light box. These are often recommended for Seasonal Affective Disorder (SAD) and are widely available at a fairly low cost.

At night you want the opposite, and to have as dark a room as possible. Ensure you have no screens or standby lights on in the bedroom. Try to avoid looking at screens at all just before bed, or wear blue-light-blocking glasses. If your phone has a night mode, which turns the screen slightly orange so that it emits less blue light, use this, as your body is less sensitive to this kind of light.

A happy, healthy you

Air

Something we all need in even greater abundance than water is air! While moving to a secluded country spot surrounded by greenery and fresh air would no doubt do us all good, for many it just isn't an option. City air, sadly, does contain pollutants, and although, even in London, the air quality is better than that of many other cities worldwide, it remains a known health risk. Respiratory and heart problems can be caused and exacerbated by pollution, and even relatively low levels of pollution can cause chronic illness, including heart disease, over prolonged periods.

What can you do? There are a few steps you can take to limit your exposure to pollution, including limiting time in built up areas where possible (not always practical), wearing a mask, particularly if you cycle or walk/run through urban areas when you will be breathing more deeply and are close to traffic, and ensuring you have plenty of antioxidants in your diet to help combat the impact of the toxins on your body.

Plants are also a wonderful thing to have in the home! There are a number that help to clean the air by removing chemicals, bacteria and viruses, as well as improving oxygen levels. NASA even conducted research on the topic. The plants they recommended to help improve air quality in the home included:

- English ivy
- Peace lilies
- Bamboo palms
- Variegated snake plants
- Some dracaenas
- Some daisies and chrysanthemums

As well as absorbing carbon dioxide and releasing oxygen, all of these plants help remove benzene, formaldehyde and trichloroethylene from the air. These three chemicals are all carcinogens (they increase the risk of certain cancers).

Furthermore, research has shown a link between both green spaces and indoor plants, and improved mental health, so having a few of our green friends around can help us stay healthy in multiple ways!

Water

Water is life! We all need it; we all use and drink it daily. Most people don't drink enough of it, in fact; the average adult needs between 1.5 and 2 litres a day. That in itself is a challenge and something you should think about and work on building up to if you don't currently drink enough.

But we should also think about the quality of the water we drink. The chances are you will be on mains water that has been heavily filtered and cleaned with chemicals. While the UK's tap water is among the cleanest in the world and has to comply with extremely strict standards, it does still contain chemicals. Chlorine is the main chemical present in tap water, as it is added as a disinfectant, but there may also be traces of lead (predominantly from old piping), and some areas add additional fluoride to the water. While fluoride is needed for healthy teeth, too much can cause fluorosis, which is permanent damage and discolouration. (It is worth noting that exposure to fluoride is predominantly due to toothpaste rather than tap water.)

Perhaps more concerning than the above is that tests have shown small amounts of drugs and hormones in tap water in the UK. This is because all water, including that from our toilets, goes back into the system, so drugs (including the widely used contraceptive pill, which contains the hormone oestrogen) are able to get into our water system. While the levels are very low, the long-term impact on our health of consuming water containing these substances just isn't known. A rather alarming fact that we do know, however, is that official research by the Department for Environment, Food & Rural Affairs a number of years ago found large numbers of male fish are changing sex due to levels of hormones seeping into our rivers.

So, what can you do about it? Is bottled water better? Well, the health issue with bottled water is that it is contained in soft plastic bottles, many of which contain Bisphenol A (BPA), a chemical that can be irritating to the respiratory system and is known to be a hormone disruptor. It acts a little like oestrogen in the body, disrupting natural hormone balance, which could impact fertility. Some research has also been suggestive of links between BPA and cancer, given its ability to cause cellular damage. Aside from BPA, bottled water is extremely expensive compared to tap water, and has an environmental impact due to the use of plastic bottles and transportation from source. Overall, it is not a sustainable option on an individual or environmental level.

The best option appears to be the use of a home filter to remove as many of the contaminants from tap water as possible. These come in a range of styles, from simple water jugs such as those by Brita, to larger-scale carbon filters such as Berkey, to fully plumbed-in systems. There is of course a cost differential between these, and my personal research led me to choose the middle option of a large carbon-based filter. This is not too much of an upfront cost, and as filters don't need to be replaced regularly, there are no additional costs for a number of years. I find the taste of the filtered water more pleasant than that straight from the tap, and I gain comfort from knowing the substance that I am consuming in large quantities, day in, day out, is as clean as possible.

Household toxins

We are surrounded by chemicals in the home, from cleaning products, paint and fuels, to toiletries and cosmetics. While it would take huge dedication to live entirely chemical/toxin-free, there are some simple things you can do to reduce exposure. The first is being aware of where toxins may be found.

Some of the more serious toxins may be somewhat integrated into your home, for example, asbestos in old buildings, heavy metals (such as lead pipes), and paint and mould, particularly in older and damp buildings. These can all have quite significant effects on health. Dealing with them can be time-consuming and costly, but be on the lookout for signs and treat any issues that you become aware of. Mould occurs due to excess moisture, so make sure you get fresh air into the house as much as possible, ensure sufficient insulation and warmth, dry laundry outside and allow bathrooms to dry out well to limit growth. Mould is a recognised allergen and irritant, and can be a particular issue for those suffering from respiratory issues including asthma. Be aware of mould building up in damp places like washing machines, the inside of bath toys, and around sinks and windows.

The next category of potential toxins is household cleaning products. In our era of excess hygiene, we're all too quick to spray chemicals around the home. There are a number of more eco/health-friendly brands now available, but do always check the label to see what they really contain. Sometimes simple, natural products are a superb and cheap alternative too. Here's a few ideas:

- Use an eco-egg or soap nuts in your washing machine instead of detergent.
- A number of essential oils are antibacterial, antifungal and/or antiviral. Two of my favourites are tea tree essential oil and oregano essential oil. Both are strong and need diluting before use. Avoid getting them directly on the skin. You can make a simple spray by adding a few drops of either one (or a combination of both) to a 50:50 mix of basic vinegar and cooled boiled water. You could also add other essential oils, such as lavender or lemon, if you like the smell.
- For tough spots of dirt, sprinkle with bicarbonate of soda before using the vinegar spray. Bicarbonate of soda is also a good deodoriser (think smelly trainers, rubbish bins or bad odours in the fridge!).
- Vinegar also works well as a fabric softener and dishwasher rinse aid, which is especially useful if you live in a hard water area.

In the kitchen be aware of BPA (as discussed in the *Water* section). It is found in soft plastics, so always buy BPA-free food containers and water bottles. Also look out for PFOA (perfluorooctanoic acid), found in Teflon, which can cause issues with the immune system in particular.

The other main area where you are likely to find toxins in the home is in your toiletries and cosmetics. Many of the substances used in personal care products are considered to be hormone disruptors, also known as xenoestrogens. These can block or mimic hormones in the body, sending the natural hormonal system out of balance. There have been links to a number of health issues as a result, including cancer, although research on specific products is generally not definitive given the enormous range of chemicals used in different products. The safety rules for chemicals that are allowed to be used in the EU are also strict, but all the same, some chemical types may be best avoided. Increasingly the health industry is becoming aware of this, and there are more and more 'free-from' products available. Here are a few key chemicals to look out for:
- Parabens: used as a preservative, these can act like oestrogen in the body.
- Phthalates: commonly found in nail polish and hair spray, these are also hormone disruptors.
- Aluminium: found in anti-perspirants (but not natural deodorants). The research is still very mixed on the potential link between aluminium and cancer, but research does suggest it can impact cognitive function and may be a factor in Alzheimer's/dementia. Aluminium is a coagulant that blocks sweat glands. But remember, sweating is an important way for the body to naturally remove toxins.

- Talc: used not just in talcum powder, but also in a number of face powders and cosmetics. Some research has shown a link between talc and ovarian cancer.
- Sodium Laureth Sulfate (SLS): used mostly to make things foam, for example shampoo, SLS can contain small levels of the carcinogen dioxane.

While research linking all of the above to disease, including cancer, is generally fairly limited, it would seem apparent that there is a degree of risk – so why take it? When there are plenty of good 'free-from' options now on the market, why not switch?

It is worth highlighting that there is currently no legal standard in place for organic cosmetics, toiletries and other non-food items. Bodies like the Soil Association do certify non-food products, so look out for their logo, but it is worth being aware that products can claim to be 'organic' or 'natural' even when they only contain a tiny percentage of organic ingredients. For example, an 'organic' shampoo may be made with 2 per cent organic essential oils, but the other 98 per cent may be full of chemicals! Rather ridiculous and worth being aware of.

Drugs and medicines

I wouldn't suggest for one moment anyone ignores their doctor's advice and refuses to take prescribed medication. Modern Western medicine is an incredible scientific feat that is constantly evolving and has saved very many lives.

However, there are cases where over-the-counter or prescription medications are taken perhaps a little too keenly, and people may forget about, or be unaware of, more natural alternatives that could help instead.

There are many excellent books and resources dedicated to this topic, and I am not going to go into any sort of detail here on natural complementary or alternative medicines, but I wanted to highlight the issue to make people a little more mindful of what they are taking. Pain, inflammation, PMT, allergies, IBS/gut upsets, poor sleep, high cholesterol, fatigue and high blood pressure are among the many issues for which nutritional therapists use diet and potentially supplements to help support the body. I'd encourage anyone who regularly uses short-term medication, or is on long-term medication, to look into some of the more natural ways you may be able to support your health; food can be a powerful healing tool!

'You are

what you

eat'

Part three:

Nourish your body
with the best food

As I was studying nutrition when I was diagnosed with cancer, turning to diet as a key way to help support my body was an obvious choice. I was already a healthy eater, but I did make a few adjustments to what I ate. Here I share the focus and fundamentals of my diet, as they are valid for anyone wanting to eat well and nourish their body.

I do want to say here that there is no diet that is proven to either prevent or cure cancer. However, there is plenty of research showing that certain foods do increase the risk of some cancers, or cause damage to the body in some way, while other foods support the body, by improving immunity or reducing inflammation for example, and these are the facts that my diet is based on.

My attitude to food is *everything in moderation*. Before my diagnosis, I followed this diet around 80 per cent of the time, and in the other 20 per cent I ate stuff that was, while maybe not as good for my body, enjoyable and good for my happiness/mental health! Yes, I love a glass of champagne or an indulgent dessert as much as the next person! I don't believe in banning any foods, as restriction is hard, boring and almost impossible to maintain for the long term. Instead I think you should focus on getting all the good things into your diet. If you focus on what you *can* eat, the other stuff just won't seem as important. So here are my top tips on what to fill your body with to nourish it and stay healthy.

The focus of my diet is unrefined whole foods, with loads of plants. I eat seasonal and organic produce as much as possible to ensure freshness and maximum nutrients (with the ethical and environmental positives being a bonus). I don't eat meat (I stopped eating it after my original colon operation), as I feel better without it, and I minimise anything processed or refined (especially sugar), and dairy. So, the below is what makes up the vast majority of my diet, and what I believe should be the majority of everyone's diet, regardless of your health!

A happy, healthy you

1. Vegetables and fruit

We all know vegetables and fruit contain vitamins and minerals (there is more detail on these later in this chapter). These are compounds that the body cannot make itself, but that are required for it to function properly. On top of this, plants also contain phytonutrients. While similar in some ways to vitamins, phytonutrients aren't necessary for our bodies to function, but they are very beneficial. Different vegetables and fruit contain different nutrients, and nature is extremely clever, as the different colours of produce are often reflective of these. This is why it is often said you should eat the rainbow; by consuming a variety of different-coloured fruits and vegetables, you will ensure you get a wide range of nutrients.

I aim for ten portions of fruit and vegetables a day. A portion is around a handful, so a small apple, a medium tomato, a couple of broccoli florets or a peach would each be one portion. In grams, it's around 70–80g, although for uncooked leaves (salad, spinach, etc.) it will be less than this. Fruit juice does count, but you should only have one portion of this a day. Although the vitamins and minerals are there (especially in fresh juice), by removing the pulp, you are taking away the fibre, which is a key benefit of vegetables and fruit. Try to make the majority of your ten portions vegetables, as it's important to be mindful of the sugar content of fruit. While ten portions may sound like a lot, it's very achievable if you get into the right habits. Here are my top tips:

1. Start your day with a smoothie.
Breakfast can be such an easy way to get two or three portions of fruit or vegetables, but how many of you just have a cup of coffee and toast?! Maybe you add fruit juice to feel healthy, but you are much better off swapping this for a smoothie or mixed fruit and vegetable juice. I try to stick to a simple formula of two vegetables (e.g. spinach, celery, cucumber, carrots) and one fruit (pretty much anything! Bananas and avocados give a lovely, creamy smoothie texture). Fresh ginger, lemon and lime juice can also provide extra flavour, and adding a spoonful of natural or coconut yogurt is great for smoothies. Ginger and turmeric are great anti-inflammatory ingredients. Try adding peppermint to aid digestion, or linseed (flaxseed) for omega-3 essential fatty acids. Use a blender rather than juicer, so you aren't removing all the fibre from the fruit and vegetables, (although be aware, even blending breaks down fibre, removing some of the benefits versus eating whole fruit and vegetables.)

2. Add fruit or vegetables to your breakfast.
Sticking with breakfast, there are so many ways to incorporate fruit and vegetables. Do you like to start the day with something sweet? Add fresh berries to your cereal, yogurt or overnight

A happy, healthy you

oats, or poached fruit (stone fruit, pears, apples) to porridge in winter. Top pancakes and waffles with any fruit you fancy, or even make pancakes from bananas. More of a savoury fan? Avocado on toast will probably never go out of fashion, and grilled tomatoes and mushrooms perfectly accompany eggs.

3. Make your snacks fruit- or vegetable-based.
Try making hummus with added vegetables, like roast beetroot or carrot, then eating it with vegetable crudités. Fruit always makes a good snack, and for something different, try drying out slices of apple in the oven. Slices of apple, fresh or dried, are particularly good dipped in nut butter too.

4. Have soup for lunch.
I could eat soup for lunch every day. From thick and warming root vegetable soups in winter to cold gazpacho in summer, the variations are endless, and it is easy to tick off two portions of vegetables in a bowlful. Or make a big, filling salad with some pulses or grains like quinoa, brown rice or lentils.

5. Go for vegetable-heavy dinners.
Always have at least three different vegetables for dinner, whether this is with meat or fish, in a curry or with a pasta dish. Two of my favourite dinners that can easily provide three or more portions of vegetables are stir fries and noodle bowls. Both benefit from the fact that you can use any combination of vegetables you like. Serve with brown rice noodles and top with protein of your choice (e.g. meat, fish, tofu) and a handful of fresh herbs if you have them.

6. Finish off with a fruity dessert.
If you have a sweet tooth, give in to the craving in a healthy way. Crumbles are particularly good throughout autumn and winter, as are simple baked apples or poached pears. In the summer try fruit salad, a soft fruit fool made with natural yogurt, or healthy homemade jelly made with fruit juice, fresh fruit and agar flakes, a sea vegetable that is a natural gelling agent. See the recipe section of this book for more details.

Try to eat the freshest produce you can, as nutrients are depleted over time. The best way to do this is by focusing on local/seasonal produce. Frozen is also a great option, as produce is frozen so soon after picking that nutrients are well preserved. Avoid produce that is cooked before freezing, though, as this will have depleted the nutrient content.

Personally, I eat organic food as much as possible in order to avoid the chemicals that are often heavily used for non-organic produce – but how important is it, and is it worth the extra cost? Firstly, it is important to understand what organic produce actually is. Organic means avoiding fertilisers and pesticides, and instead using husbandry techniques to control pests and disease, and to maintain soil fertility (note: a limited number of approved products and substances are allowed in the processing of organic food). In Europe, a product can only be labelled as organic if it has been inspected and certified by an official control body. In the UK there are nine of these, including the Soil Association, which is one of the best-known. Organic is positive for the environment and for our bodies in its limited use of chemical nasties, and for me, it is definitely something to strive towards from an environmental and personal perspective. However, organic produce is generally more expensive, so just isn't attainable for everyone. In my view, if it's a choice between fewer organic vegetables, or more, non-organic vegetables, the latter is better! A healthy diet full of varied vegetables and fruit is more important to prioritise than buying only organic, which is a nice extra to have on top.

It is also worth noting that you can get amazing, local, naturally grown produce that is not certified organic. Many small producers follow natural growing methods and avoid the use of pesticides, but are not registered organic. Why? Well, gaining certification is a timely and costly process. It can take years to become fully certified and this is just too restrictive for some smaller producers.

Ultimately, try to buy mindfully and get the best quality you can afford. Try to learn more about the origins of what you are eating. Do you know how and where it was produced? Also, do compare prices. For some items (mushrooms are a good example), organic options are usually pretty much the same price as non-organic. For some more exotic items, there may not be an organic option at all. So, pick and choose, perhaps aim for organic for cheaper items that you eat regularly, and don't worry so much for things that are just an occasional treat.

2. Pulses, grains and other plants

Like fruit and vegetables, other plants also contain valuable nutrients. Pulses, including lentils and chickpeas, as well as unrefined grains and pseudo grains including rice, quinoa, millet and spelt, are important staples for me. They are good sources of fibre, protein and carbohydrate and make a great base for so many dishes.

3. Lean meat, fish and eggs

While I don't personally eat meat, lean meat (in moderation) is a great source of protein and various micronutrients including iron and B12 (which is found only in animal products). When it comes to fish, I focus on oily fish (salmon, mackerel, anchovies, herring, sardines), for the omega-3 essential fatty acid content, although I'm also partial to seafood, which has the benefit of being a great source of zinc. When it comes to animal produce, I am very strict about eating only organic. Putting aside the ethical arguments, organic certification strictly limits the use of artificial hormones and medicines for the animals, and, quite honestly, I wouldn't want these in my body. Again, I appreciate that organic may not be a viable option for all, but I strongly believe it is best to eat less, but better-quality, animal produce as far as possible.

See later in this chapter for more information on protein.

4. Healthy fats

Fat is essential for our body, but it is important to get the right types. We need the essential fatty acids, which are also called omega-3 and omega-6, ideally in a fairly balanced ratio. Most people get plenty of omega-6, which is found in vegetable oils, meat and most processed foods, but not much omega-3, which is found in oily fish like salmon and mackerel, as well as various seeds including linseed (flaxseed) and hemp seeds. Nuts, seeds, avocados and olives/olive oil are all other great sources of healthy fats such as oleic acid.

See later in this chapter for more information on fats.

5. Prebiotics/probiotics

Did you know that around 60–70 per cent of your immune system is in your gut? You may have heard of the microbiome, which is the host of bacteria that live in your body. A healthy microbiome is essential for immunity, nutrient absorption and general gut health. New research emerges frequently about the importance of the microbiome, and what you eat has a huge influence on its diversity and health. Pre- and probiotics are an important part of this. Prebiotics are a form of dietary fibre that essentially feed the microbiome, while probiotics contain strains of live bacteria.

Prebiotics are found in any foods with fibre: vegetables, fruits, pulses and grains, for example. The wider the variety of these you consume, the more you'll be supporting a diverse microbiome. Research suggests these make a longer-term difference than probiotics.

Probiotics are most prevalent in fermented foods: natural live/cultured yogurt and kefir, kombucha (a fermented tea drink), sauerkraut, kimchi and (to a lesser degree because it has been baked) sourdough bread are all great options. You can also buy probiotic supplements, but getting them via food is preferable in the long term. Do be careful if you are on chemotherapy or other treatments, though. With a lowered immune system, you are at higher risk of infection, so you may be advised to avoid fermented foods because of the bacteria.

——

So, what do I minimise my intake of? (I would never say 'completely avoid' – again, it's all about moderation, and I never want eating to become a miserable and stressful process!)

1. Processed foods.
If you don't recognise the ingredients, it's likely your body won't either! Processed foods are often high in salt, refined sugar and trans fats, all of which are damaging to the body in various ways. Of course, they are convenient, and are designed to be addictively tasty, but processed foods shouldn't be a staple part of anyone's diet. Save them for occasional treats instead!

2. Refined sugar.
This is a big focus of many anti-cancer diets, as it is understood that cancer cells need a lot of glucose to feed on. However, high sugar intake is not good for anyone, with well-researched links to obesity, diabetes and cardiovascular issues, among other problems. You should also be very careful if switching to unrefined sugars, such as maple, agave or rice syrup, etc. Whilst they may be slightly better in terms of the blood-sugar spike they can cause, and some even contain low levels of nutrients, they are still sugar, so consume in moderation.

3. White flour.
Highly refined white wheat flour is widely used in the Western world and is of very limited nutritional value. It is high in gluten, which can be inflammatory, and is easily broken down to sugar. While I don't suggest it is necessary for the average healthy person to cut out all white flour, it is an ingredient to be mindful of, particularly for anyone with any kind of

inflammatory or chronic disease. Wholemeal flour is nutritionally better, although it is still a very refined and high-gluten grain, so I prefer to replace it with less refined alternatives, such as rye or spelt flour/bread, and substitute wheat pasta with rice or chickpea pasta, for example.

4. Dairy.
Dairy is meant for growing young cows! As such it is high in hormones and insulin growth factor which *may* promote cancerous cell growth. Research is still somewhat questionable on the link between dairy and cancer, but dairy does have other issues. It contains proteins that the human body is not designed to break down (most importantly casein and lactose), and so intolerances to these are not uncommon. As with wheat flour, I'm not suggesting everyone should cut out all dairy, but the Western diet is heavily reliant on it, and it is an ingredient to be mindful of. Try not to eat it in vast quantities or with every meal. There are so many easily available and tasty alternatives to milk, yogurt and even cheese and ice cream, it's worth giving some of them a go.

5. Red and processed meats.
There are proven links between these and the increased risk of certain cancers, particularly bowel cancer. While red meat is a superb source of iron, the human body really does not need to eat meat every day. It would benefit both our bodies and the planet if we all cut down on meat consumption just a little.

The importance of protein

Protein is essential for the growth and maintenance of all body tissues, including muscles, bone, skin and blood. Protein is also needed for the production of hormones and enzymes, to support the immune system, and to maintain important balances in the body, including fluid and pH balance. In an average-weight person, protein makes up about 20 per cent of body mass. While everyone needs protein, its role in growth and repair makes it especially important for growing children, pregnant women, those who exercise a lot and those recovering from an injury. It's also very important when dealing with many chronic illnesses.

Dietary Sources of Protein
Protein is made up of amino acids. The body commonly uses about 20 amino acids, and nine of these are essential; this means that the body cannot make them, so you need to get them through your diet. When we talk about food sources of protein, we generally divide them into

complete and complementary sources. Complete proteins contain all of those nine essential amino acids, roughly in the proportion that the body needs them, while complementary proteins don't contain them all, or are lower in some.

Animal proteins (that includes meat, poultry, fish, dairy and eggs) are complete proteins, while most plant sources are complementary. This doesn't make them 'worse' sources, it is just important that, if you don't eat animal proteins, you consume a variety of plant-based proteins to ensure you get all of the different amino acids.

Approximate grams of protein per portion	
Animal sources	Plant-based sources
Meat (30g protein per 100g)	Quinoa (a complete protein) (14g protein per 100g)
Poultry (30g protein per 100g)	Pulses: Lentils, chickpeas, beans and peas (8g protein per 100g)
Fish (20–25g protein per 100g)	Tofu (8g protein per 100g)
Eggs (12g protein per 2 large eggs)	Nuts and seeds (8–10g protein per 50g)
Dairy: Cheddar cheese (12g protein per 50g)	Oats (11g protein per 100g)
Dairy: milk and yogurt (3–5g protein per 100g)	Rice, other grains and many vegetables all also contain a certain amount of protein, but don't rely on them as your only source

How much protein do you need?

The UK daily guidelines call for 0.75g protein for every kilogram of body weight. For example, someone weighing 60kg would need 50g protein from their diet each day. EU guidelines are slightly higher, at 0.83g protein per kilogram of body weight. Guidance is also higher for children, athletes and pregnant or breastfeeding women. These guides are for the minimum amount that is considered necessary to avoid risks associated with a protein deficiency. The average Western diet actually includes a significantly higher amount of protein. While there are risks associated with having too much protein, the World Health Organisation advises that consuming up to twice the guideline amount is likely to be without risk.

Many of the issues associated with excess protein intake are specific to the consumption of animal protein. This is because these products are generally also fairly high in saturated fat, so may encourage weight gain. A high protein intake can also increase the work of the kidneys, because they are instrumental in the breakdown of protein. An excess intake may therefore increase the risk of kidney disease. Research has also shown links between high animal protein intake and increased risk of heart disease, as well as links to certain cancers.

The key takeaway when it comes to protein? Make sure you have varied sources, particularly if you follow a plant-based diet, and eat protein with each meal, as it will help you feel full. But don't go overboard. Very few people for example, need to add protein powders or shakes into their diet, and try to be mindful of the portion size of protein. A useful guide is the palm of your hand – a portion of protein should be roughly the same size.

A happy, healthy you

Understanding fats

Fats: they're bad, they're good, they're saturated, monounsaturated, polyunsaturated, trans, cis, hydrogenated… the so called 'advice' and media around this macronutrient are endless. It can be very confusing!

So, are fats bad? No! Well, not all of them. In fact, fats are essential for a variety of functions in the body. They are components of cell membranes (and are particularly important in the brain); they are needed for cell-to-cell communication and for the protection of vital organs; and they are also used for storage and production of energy. Of course, too much fat, just like too much of any kind of food, will lead to weight gain. Excess fat is stored easily in the body, but remember, excess protein and carbohydrates can also be turned into triglycerides (the storage form of fat). One thing to keep in mind, though, is that, gram for gram, fat is the most calorie-dense macro-nutrient, at 9 calories per gram, compared to 4 calories per gram for carbohydrates and protein. So, you need some fat, but not too much. How do you know which ones to consume and which to avoid?

To help you understand which fats are good and bad, and what happens to them in the body, I want to explain a little bit of chemistry – don't worry, I'll keep it simple! Fats are made up of chains of two elements, hydrogen and carbon (plus an acid on the end, but we won't go into that here). In **saturated fats** (found, for example, in butter, coconut oil, fat on meats and in egg yolks), there are single bonds between each atom. This makes them fairly stable and is why they are solid at room temperature. They are best for cooking, because they are more able to withstand high temperatures without being damaged. In **unsaturated fats**, there are some double bonds, which make the chain 'kinked'. This is essentially what makes these fats liquid at room temperature. It also makes them more prone to damage, so they go bad (rancid) more easily, which can set off a chain reaction of damage in your body as they act as free radicals. Being unsaturated doesn't make fats bad per se, but you need to be aware of their properties when you think about using added fats (i.e. oils, etc.) in cooking. Many of the problems with fats lie in how they have been treated. For example, oil that has been heated to a high temperature for frying can cause problems in the body because it has been destabilised, resulting in the production of free radicals, which are bad for the body.

Back to the terms you may hear, or see on packaging; **monounsaturated fats** only have one double bond, while **polyunsaturated fats** have at least two. Cis and trans refer to the formation of these bonds. **Cis fats** are the ones found in nature, while **trans fats** are unnatural and can cause more harm in the body, so these are the ones you really want to avoid! Trans fats can be created when fats are **hydrogenated,** so again, these are fats to stay away from.

So far, it sounds like saturated fats are the good guys, but you are probably aware that they are also what we are generally told to limit (UK guidelines recommend limiting saturated fats to a maximum of 11 per cent of your daily energy intake). This is because significant amounts of research have shown correlations between diets high in saturated fats and higher rates of death from heart disease, as saturated fat appears to raise LDL cholesterol (this is considered the 'bad' cholesterol). However, some recent research questions this link, suggesting the correlation between saturated fat intake and heart disease is not actually significant. The jury is still out on this one, but there is certainly a lot of research that suggests limiting saturated fat is a good idea.

Essential Fatty Acids – the good guys!

Earlier, I mentioned omega-3 and omega-6 fats, or the essential fatty acids (EFAs). These are polyunsaturated fats that the body needs but is unable to make. The average Western diet gets plenty of omega-6 fats, as these are abundant in most plant and vegetable oils (including sunflower oil, which is widely used in processed foods) as well as meat and dairy. Many people, however, are short of omega-3s, which are found in oily fish, linseed (flaxseed), hemp seeds and walnuts.

The ratio of omega-3 to -6 oils is important for the body, and ideally this should be close to 1:1 (although guidelines recommend a maximum one omega-3 to four omega-6). The average Western diet is actually closer to 1:12, which is far too high in omega-6 relative to omega-3. To limit omega-6, avoid lots of fried and processed food, and to increase omega-3, have 2–3 portions of oily fish a week if you eat fish (think SMASH: salmon, mackerel, anchovies, sardines and herring), or add a spoonful of linseed (flaxseed) or hemp seeds to your smoothie or porridge each morning. You need to grind both first, though, as the body is unable to break down and use the whole seed. Omega-3 fats are generally anti-inflammatory and anti-clotting, which is why fish oil capsules are often recommended for inflammatory conditions.

A happy, healthy you

Using and storing fats in the kitchen

When it comes to cooking, especially at high temperatures, saturated fats (e.g. butter, ghee and coconut oil) are best, as they are least likely to be damaged by the heat. If you want to use something like olive oil, add it after cooking, or do so at a low temperature. For example, when stir-frying, add a little water to the pan first (don't add water to hot fat or it may spit and burn you). The water will prevent the oil from getting too hot and causing damage. You should always avoid letting oil get so hot that it smokes.

Oxygen (in the air), light and heat all turn oils rancid (this makes them taste bad, but also causes damage in the body), so always store fats and oils at a cool temperature and away from light. Good-quality oil should be sold in a dark-coloured bottle (to keep light out). You'll often find this is the case with olive oil but, sadly, it is rarely so with coconut oil, so make sure you keep it in a cool, dark cupboard. If your kitchen is warm, it is better to keep oils in the fridge. Less stable oils, like flaxseed oil, should always be refrigerated, and are actually best kept in the freezer as they have such a low melting point. The same goes for oil supplements, e.g. fish oil capsules; keep these in the fridge too. If you are being really pedantic, raw nuts and seeds are also best kept in the fridge, but as long as you aren't keeping them for very long periods, a cool, dark cupboard is generally fine!

The question of sugar

Sugar gets a bad reputation and, earlier in this chapter, I touched on the detrimental effects of excess sugar. But the fact is, sugar (specifically glucose) is the body's preferred source of energy and is essential in the diet. The key is understanding the forms sugar is found in and which ones you should try to limit.

What do we mean by sugar?

When you think of sugar, you will probably firstly think of sucrose (refined or table sugar), and perhaps fructose (the form in which sugar is found in fruit). Fructose, along with glucose and galactose, are monosaccharides. These are what the body likes to absorb, and what more complex sugars are broken down into.

However, sugar is also found in other foods, such as dairy and carbohydrates (yes, even the healthy, wholegrain varieties!). In dairy produce, sugar is found in the form of lactose (which breaks down to glucose and galactose), while carbohydrates are polysaccharides (substances made of many sugar units, which are broken down into various combinations of fructose, glucose and galactose). So, you see, you get sugar from many sources that you wouldn't necessarily think of as sugar.

I like to divide sugar into free sugars and non-free sugars. The former are sugars not bound to other substances, for example table sugar, as well as all the refined sugar alternatives, such as agave, maple, rice and date syrups, coconut sugar and honey. Are these alternatives better for you? I'm afraid that, from a nutritional perspective, the answer is pretty much no. Yes, they may contain trace elements of some minerals, but you'd need huge quantities for these to amount to a level that provided health benefits. Some may also have a slightly lower impact on spiking blood glucose, but they are all very easily broken down into simple sugar molecules, so this spike will still occur. They are also all still high in calories – too many of which, we all know, will lead to weight gain. Fructose especially is easier for the body to turn into fat than glucose (so keep away from anything containing high-fructose corn syrup!)

Non-free sugars, on the other hand, are those that are bound to other substances, for example fibre (in wholegrains, vegetables and fruit), or fat and protein in dairy. These are not broken down to simple sugar molecules as quickly in the body, so don't cause the same blood glucose spike. And, of course, you are benefiting from the nutrients present in the rest of the food they are in.

The only exception I would make in the sugar debate is honey, which has been shown to have antimicrobial and antioxidant properties (I find a spoonful for a sore throat, or a little dabbed on a sore spot or wound, very helpful). But you must be mindful of the type of honey you buy. Only raw (unpasteurised) honey has health benefits, and unfortunately much of the 'honey' for sale is little more than caramelised table sugar. Heating raw honey will kill off its antioxidant and antimicrobial properties, so don't use it for cooking. As with any free sugar, I wouldn't advise using it in large quantities. Honey contains a high concentration of fructose and there is still an ongoing debate about the impact this has on your digestive system in concentrated quantities. (If you suffer from IBS, you may be advised to cut honey from your diet altogether.)

Understanding more about vitamins and minerals

We all know vitamins and minerals are extremely important for maintaining good health, so here is a short guide to why you need them, some good sources for getting them through food, and some top tips on when and how to take supplements.

Vitamins

Vitamins cannot be manufactured by the body, so must be consumed in the diet (vitamin D is something of an exception). Vitamins are needed for many bodily functions, including metabolic actions and energy production (although they cannot directly be converted into energy – you need calories for that). While whole foods are abundant in vitamins, processed and refined foods lack them, making vitamin insufficiencies and deficiencies increasingly common in the average Western diet today. An insufficiency is when the body does not have enough to function optimally (although there may not be any symptoms), while a deficiency prevents functioning altogether, potentially leading to disease.

It is worth thinking about vitamins in two groups:
* Water-soluble vitamins (C and the eight different B vitamins)
* Fat-soluble vitamins (A, D, E, K)

Water-soluble vitamins cannot be stored in the body. This means that the body needs a steady supply. The body can, however, build up stores of fat-soluble vitamins. The solubility impacts potential toxicity; you are unlikely to have excess vitamin C or B. It is pretty much impossible to have too much vitamin C or B from diet alone, although it you consume too much in the form of supplements you may experience side effects. Some fat-soluble vitamins, on the other hand, can be toxic in too-high dosages, as they can build up in the body. Again, this is unlikely to be an issue from diet alone, but it is worth bearing in mind if you also take supplements.

Key vitamins: functions and food sources

This is far from a complete list of functions or sources, but highlights the key ones it is worth understanding.

Vitamin A
For: eye health and immune function. The plant form (beta-carotene) also has an antioxidant action.
Found in: liver, egg yolk, dairy, yellow/orange fruit and vegetables and dark green vegetables.

B vitamins
For: energy production. Many are also important for detoxification.
Found in:
B1 (Thiamine): potatoes, wholegrains, meat and fish, nuts and seeds, soy beans.
B2 (Riboflavin): meat and fish, wholegrains, dairy and eggs, nuts and seeds.
B3 (Niacin): meat and fish, mushrooms, leafy greens, nuts, wholegrains.
B5 (Pantothenic Acid): beef, poultry, wholegrains, potatoes, mushrooms, tomatoes, broccoli.
B6 (Pyridoxine): purple fruit, green vegetables, potatoes, meat, fish.
B7 (Biotin): egg yolk, oats, soy beans, yeast, organ meats.
B9 (Folate): legumes, green leafy vegetables, citrus fruit.
B12 (Cobalamins): organ meats, fish, eggs, dairy – only found in foods of animal origin.
A number of vegan products, such as soy and nut milks, are fortified with B12.

Note: Being water soluble, B vitamins are easily lost when food is cooked, especially in water. Try to steam rather than boil vegetables to help preserve their vitamins.

Vitamin C (Ascorbic Acid)
For: a good immune system. Vitamin C is an important antioxidant.
Found in: many fruits and vegetables, and particularly high in citrus, berries, peppers, and dark green vegetables.

Vitamin D
For: strong bones and the immune system.
Found in: oily fish is the best dietary source, but the majority of your vitamin D is synthesised by sunshine!

Vitamin E
For: This is a powerful antioxidant.
Found in: vegetable oils, nuts and seeds, green leafy vegetables, fish.

Vitamin K
For: blood clotting.
Found in: green leafy vegetables, such as spinach and sprouts.

——

Minerals

Like vitamins, minerals must be consumed in the diet. There are many different minerals. Some, known as trace elements, are only found in tiny quantities, and their functions in the body are still somewhat unknown. However, there are a number of key minerals, which I will highlight below, that are well known to be essential to human health.

As with vitamins, *dietary* intake is key, and it is important not to rely on supplements to make sure you get adequate quantities (although, administered correctly, mineral supplementation can be very effective in supporting health). As with the fat-soluble vitamins, you can have too much of a good thing, and excess levels of some minerals can be toxic. It is also worth noting that a number of minerals compete with one another for absorption into the body, so an excess of one can in fact cause a deficiency of another. Copper and zinc are two good examples of this.

Key minerals: functions and food sources

Iron is very important in the body, as is a key constituent of blood. It attaches to oxygen within red blood cells to carry it round the body, which is why low iron levels can make you feel tired. However, it is not a good idea to take iron supplements unless you have had blood tests that show your iron levels are low. This is because iron is very toxic to the body in too-high quantities. It is pro-inflammatory and is required for bacteria to survive in the body. Iron is lost from the body in blood (which is why women of menstrual age need far higher iron intakes than men and pre/post-menopausal women), and a very small amount in stools, but the body actually has no active physiological way of excreting iron if stores get too high. In fact, it can be a good idea for healthy individuals (especially men) who eat a lot of red meat or a high-iron diet to give blood regularly to manage the body's iron levels!

There are two types of iron. One, haem iron, is found only in 'flesh foods' (meat, fish and poultry) and this form is absorbed most easily. The other type, non-haem iron, is found in both plant and flesh foods (despite some popular opinion, research has shown that vegetarians have similar levels of iron in their blood to meat eaters and are no more likely to suffer from iron deficiency anaemia). Non-haem iron makes up most of our dietary iron intake, and although it is not as easily absorbed as haem iron, its absorption can increase by up to six times when vitamin C is consumed at the same time. Some of the best sources of iron are meat, dark green leafy vegetables, apricots and sunflower and pumpkin seeds. It is also worth noting a number of substances decrease the absorption of iron. These include oxalates (particularly high in spinach and rhubarb), large quantities of calcium (this is particularly relevant for infants, who have a high calcium diet, so it is key that they get enough iron in their diet when weaning begins), phytates (found in wholegrains, legumes, nuts and seeds), and polyphenols (high in tea, coffee and some spices).

Calcium is the most abundant mineral in the body and is vital for bone health as well as the cardiovascular and nervous systems. It is mainly found in dairy, as well as in vegetables, although it is less concentrated in the latter. Many non-dairy milks are also calcium-fortified. Calcium is very important for muscles, too. It works alongside magnesium, with calcium enabling the muscles to contract, and magnesium needed in order for them to relax. It is why you will often see calcium and magnesium sold as a combined supplement. Excess calcium can cause constipation, while excess magnesium can have a laxative effect.

Magnesium is necessary for hundreds of enzyme reactions in the body, particularly in relation to energy production, muscle relaxation and nerve impulses. It is widely available in whole foods and fruit and vegetables, particularly the dark green leafy kinds. Magnesium must be bound to something, so if you are taking supplements you should be aware of the form it is in. Magnesium oxide is generally the most common, but is one of the least absorbable forms. Magnesium citrate has higher absorption and is used in some laxatives, while amino-acid-chelated magnesium or magnesium glycinate are forms that absorb well for muscle relaxation.

Phosphorus is the second most abundant mineral in the body. It is important for energy and bone formation, and is even a component of DNA. It is a constituent of all plant and animal tissues, so deficiency is largely unknown.

Zinc is important for cell growth and immunity (which is why zinc is often recommended when you start to get a cold). It is found in protein-rich foods (such as meats, seafood and legumes) and wholegrains, as well as vegetables. However, like iron, its absorption is decreased by phytates and oxalates. Zinc competes with a number of other minerals for absorption, so long-term supplementation is not recommended as it can actually cause a deficiency of other minerals, in particular copper.

Confusingly, Government reference intakes for vitamins and minerals vary somewhat, but there are a number of factors (such as age, gender, illnesses and genetic predisposition) that all impact vitamin requirements, so there is no accurate 'right' amount for everyone. Reference values should therefore be used as just that – a reference point – rather than a precise daily requirement. Vitamins and minerals are best consumed via the diet, although good-quality supplements can be useful, especially if you follow a specific diet that may make it difficult to consume enough of certain vitamins. Here are a couple of tips to consider when taking supplements:

- Buy the best-quality supplements you can afford. Cheaper vitamins tend to contain bulking agents and fillers, which it's best to avoid if possible, and they may contain less bioavailable forms of vitamins (this means that the body cannot use them efficiently or effectively).
- Generally, vitamins are best taken with food for optimum absorption, but do check the label on whatever you are taking.
- Do not take vitamin supplements with tea or coffee. The polyphenols in these drinks destroy certain vitamins or prevent them from being absorbed.
- And one thing to remember: if you take a B-vitamin complex, or multivitamin with B2, it can turn your urine a very bright yellow – so don't be alarmed!

Phytonutrients

Phytonutrients are substances found in plants that are a little like vitamins and minerals. We do not need phytonutrients to survive (they are not essential), but they do have many very significant health benefits. Below, I have listed a few main groups of phytonutrients, along with their food sources and some of the things research suggests they may help with. You'll see me mentioning these in the recipe section of this book, too.

A happy, healthy you

Phytonutrient	Example food sources	Potential health benefits
Polyphenols	Herbs, vegetables, fruits, tea, soy, cocoa.	Often, these are what give vegetables and fruit their colours. There's a huge variety, but generally they are antioxidant, and many are anti-inflammatory, antiviral and anti-allergenic. Some have been found to be cardiovascular-protective or have anti-cancer properties.
Flavonoids (type of polyphenol)	In most plants, including fruit, vegetables and tea.	Like all polyphenols, most are antioxidant, anti-inflammatory, antiviral and anti-allergenic.
Anthocyanins (type of polyphenol)	Red and purple fruits (the darker, the better!). Fruit skins tend to have the highest concentration.	Powerful antioxidants, with potential cardiovascular-protective benefits and anti-cancer properties.
Phytoestrogens or isoflavonoids	Soy, alfalfa, legumes, chickpeas, peanuts, linseed (flaxseed) and sesame seeds.	They bind to oestrogen receptors, mimicking oestrogen effects. They can potentially protect against cardiovascular disease, osteoporosis and hormone-driven cancers. Also helpful during menopause.
Glucosinolates and isothiocyanates	Cruciferous vegetables (e.g. cabbage, cauliflower, broccoli, kale, sprouts).	They support liver detoxification pathways, and have potential anti-cancer properties, inhibiting cancer cell multiplication in lab studies.
Carotenoids, including beta-carotene (provitamin A) and lycopene	Yellow, orange, red and dark green vegetables and fruit, e.g. pumpkins, sweet potatoes, carrots, tomatoes.	Some are converted by the body into vitamin A. They are antioxidant and have shown anti-cancer properties (with the largest study being into lycopene, found in tomatoes, helping with prostate cancer).
Phytosterols	Wheat, sesame, various nuts, olive oil.	These are lipids that are similar in structure and function to cholesterol, so can help lower LDL ('bad') cholesterol levels.

An anti-inflammatory diet

While I am not going to discuss lots of different diets in this book, I do want to highlight the fundamentals of an anti-inflammatory diet, which is particularly important for anyone suffering from any kind of chronic disease. It really is just a matter of following the advice around the whole foods diet I have already discussed, including plenty of vegetables.

Inflammation is part of the body's immune response and is very important in acute situations. It can help increase blood flow to an area of injury or infection, helping with the healing process or attack process respectively. However, inflammation becomes an issue when it is chronic, i.e. when it is continuously present, which puts stress on the body. This is what tends to happen in almost all chronic illnesses, so supporting the body to lower this inflammation is important.

Diet is key in moderating and aggravating inflammation; and by diet, I mean both what and how we eat! Eating slowly and chewing thoroughly is a good place to start to allow your digestive system to work effectively. Try to limit drinking lots of fluid while eating, which can dilute stomach acid, impacting its ability to digest food. Coffee and tea should also be drunk away from mealtimes, as both contain compounds that can affect the absorption of certain nutrients. Top anti-inflammatory nutrients include vitamins A, B6, C, D and E, fibre, omega-3 essential fatty acids, magnesium and some flavonoids.

Top anti-inflammatory foods:
- Green leafy vegetables, e.g. spinach, kale, dark salad leaves.
- Cruciferous vegetables, e.g. broccoli, cauliflower, cabbages.
- Dark-coloured (pigmented) vegetables, e.g. aubergine, beetroot, peppers.
- Dark-pigmented fruit, especially berries, e.g. blueberries, blackcurrants, raspberries, pomegranate, plums.
- Oily fish for the omega-3 essential fatty acids, e.g. salmon, mackerel, anchovies, sardines, herring. (Tuna is no longer classified as an oily fish and is best limited due to high levels of heavy metals.)
- Nuts and seeds for omega-3s and vitamin E, e.g. linseed (flaxseed) and hemp seeds (particularly good sources of omega-3, and key to include if you don't eat fish), almonds, walnuts and Brazil nuts.
- Wholegrains/pseudo grains, e.g. brown rice, quinoa, buckwheat, millet, amaranth.
- Cold-pressed oils, especially olive, avocado and flaxseed (always refrigerate).
- Spices, in particular garlic, ginger and turmeric.

Foods that can aggravate inflammation:
- Fried and processed foods, especially those containing trans fats.
- Margarine and commercial seed oils.
- Free sugars, including those in sweets, cakes, sugary drinks and desserts.
- Processed meats, e.g. sausages, salami and others using nitrates/preservatives.
- Refined carbohydrates made with white flour, which are high in inflammatory gluten and easily break down into free sugar in the body.

'Nourish

to

flourish'

Part four:

Recipes to nourish

An introduction to the recipes

All of these recipes are filled with whole-food ingredients. They are free from dairy, meat and wheat, and the sweet treats are low in sugar. Everything is simple to make and there are no fancy or expensive ingredients.

Soup is such a good staple for a quick meal; nutritious, warming and easy on the digestive system. Make a batch whenever you have a little free time, then refrigerate or freeze portions for reheating when you need an instant meal.

The salad section contains nutritious and filling dishes. Forget a bunch of lettuce with a few vegetables on top! I ensure my salads have good sources of protein and healthy fats. I also add a variety of different grains to ensure a diversity of fibre to support gut health.

The main meals give a balance of protein, healthy fats and plenty of vegetables, with many being plant-based.

The sweet dishes are fruit-based, healthier options for desserts or snacks that are still delicious!

A happy, healthy you

A note on seasoning

I don't always specify adding salt to my recipes as seasoning is very much down to personal taste. I often find food too salty in restaurants as I use very little at home, but others may find some recipes bland without adding salt, as it's an excellent flavour enhancer. Too much salt is not good for you and processed foods often contain alarmingly high quantities, but do season dishes to your taste, either while cooking or at the end. Use unrefined sea or rock salt rather than refined table salt, which is sometimes bleached and will have had all minerals other than sodium and chloride removed.

A note on toasting nuts and seeds

When a fantastic group of people tested my recipes for me, one suggestion I received a few times was to toast nuts and seeds before adding them to a dish. While I agree that this can add a lovely flavour, raw nuts and seeds are a better option from a nutritional standpoint. They all contain healthy fats, which are damaged by heat, turning rancid very easily. So, I leave this one down to personal choice; toast your nuts and seeds if you prefer, but don't heat them any more than you need to!

A note on oven temperatures

All oven temperatures are based on an electric fan oven. For non-fan ovens, increase the temperature by 20°C.

Soups

A delicious, warming soup that contains a good portion of protein from the lentils and some healthy fat from the coconut milk, making it a balanced meal. Turmeric and ginger both have anti-inflammatory properties, but make sure you add black pepper, which makes the turmeric bioavailable (converts it to a form the body can use).

Curried parsnip and lentil soup

Serves 4

500g parsnips

olive oil, for drizzling

2 tsps curry powder

160g dry red lentils

400ml coconut milk

10g fresh ginger, grated, or 1 tsp ground ginger

6g fresh turmeric, grated, or ½ tsp ground turmeric

2 large celery sticks

sea salt and freshly ground black pepper

fresh coriander, chopped, to serve

Preheat the oven to 180°C/gas mark 4.

Peel and roughly chop the parsnips. Place in a baking tray. Drizzle them with olive oil and sprinkle over the curry powder, then roast for 25 minutes.

Meanwhile, rinse the lentils, then place in a large saucepan over a low heat with the coconut milk and 400ml cold water, along with the ginger and turmeric. Allow to gently simmer while the parsnips cook (don't worry if they're still a little firm when you take them out of the oven).

Chop the celery then add to the lentil mixture, along with the roasted parsnips. Simmer for around 15 minutes until the vegetables are soft.

Remove from the heat and blend using a handheld blender until smooth. Season with salt and black pepper to taste. Top with freshly chopped coriander to serve.

Watercress is vitamin- and mineral-rich, with high levels of iron, calcium and vitamins A, C and E, and its bitter properties stimulate the digestive system. Its strong, peppery flavour makes a wonderful soup. The oat cream gives a lovely, creamy texture and adds protein.

Creamy watercress soup

Serves 4

1 onion

olive oil, for frying

400g potatoes

2 garlic cloves, chopped or crushed

1.2 litres vegetable stock (homemade if possible!)

100g watercress

100ml oat cream

sea salt

Peel and chop the onion, then in a large saucepan, fry in a little oil over a low-medium heat with a generous pinch of salt for around 15 minutes, until very soft but not quite turning brown. Peel and roughly chop the potatoes and add to the onion with the garlic. Pour over the stock and simmer for about 30 minutes until the potatoes are soft.

Add the watercress and simmer for just a couple more minutes, then remove the pan from the heat. Add the oat cream, then blend using a handheld blender until smooth. Season to taste with a little sea salt and serve.

This carrot and ginger soup is deliciously warming for a cold day and contains plenty of vitamin C, along with anti-inflammatory properties thanks to the ginger. You can easily swap the shallots for red or white onions, and if you don't have fresh ginger, just use a tsp of ground ginger instead. Did you know that the old wives' tale that eating carrots could help you see in the dark comes from the fact that carrots are high in beta-carotene (provitamin A), and vitamin A is essential for good eye health?

Carrot and ginger soup

Serves 4

2 shallots

olive oil, for frying

800g carrots

2.5cm piece of fresh ginger, peeled and finely chopped

1.2 litres vegetable stock (homemade if possible!)

zest of 1 lemon

sea salt and freshly ground black pepper

Roughly chop up the shallots and carrots. In a large saucepan, fry the shallots in the olive oil over a medium heat for around 10 minutes until they soften and begin to turn golden. Add the carrots to the pan, pour over the vegetable stock and bring to the boil. Reduce the heat, add the ginger and lemon zest, and leave to simmer for 30–40 minutes.

Take the soup off the heat and blend with a handheld blender until smooth. Season with sea salt and black pepper to taste and serve.

Leeks are part of the allium (or onion) family and are high in antioxidants and anti-inflammatory compounds. They're also a super source of prebiotics, which are key for gut health. I think celeriac is a great, versatile vegetable, although granted, not the most beautiful! You can swap it for chunks of celery if you prefer. This soup has so much flavour but is actually very mild. You can increase the spice or add some fresh or ground chilli to give it a kick if you fancy. If you eat meat, try adding cooked chicken at the same time as the celeriac or instead of the leeks. This makes for a deliciously nourishing soup and is the perfect way to use up leftover chicken from a roast.

Leek and celeriac soup

Serves 4

200g celeriac

200g leeks

olive oil, for frying

1 large garlic clove, crushed

2 tsps curry powder

½ tsp paprika

½ tsp ground cumin

¼ tsp ground turmeric or 1cm piece fresh turmeric, peeled and finely grated

2cm piece of fresh ginger, peeled and finely grated

200ml coconut milk

1l stock (use good quality, organic bone broth, or homemade vegetable stock if possible)

sea salt and freshly ground black pepper

Peel and chop the celeriac into small chunks and chop the leeks into rings. Make sure you wash well between the layers.

Heat a drizzle of olive oil in a large saucepan over a low–medium heat. Add the garlic, celeriac and leeks along with the curry powder, paprika, cumin, turmeric and ginger and stir to coat. Gently fry for 5–10 minutes until the vegetables are just starting to brown.

Add the rest of the ingredients to the saucepan, stir and bring to a simmer. Leave to simmer gently for about 45 minutes until the celeriac is soft.

Remove from the heat and blend with a handheld blender until smooth. Season with salt and black pepper to taste and serve.

I was sceptical about this flavour combination until I tried it, but it quickly became a favourite! This is a real immune-boosting soup, with mushrooms (you can use any variety), garlic and ginger all having immune-supporting properties.

Mushroom and ginger soup

Serves 4

½ onion

2 garlic cloves

thumb-size piece of
   fresh ginger

200g mushrooms

1 medium-sized potato

olive oil, for frying

1 litre vegetable stock

sea salt and freshly
   ground black pepper

Peel and roughly chop the onion, garlic and ginger and roughly chop the mushrooms and potatoes. Heat a little oil over a medium heat. Add the onion and garlic with a good pinch of salt and fry. Once they are soft and the onion is turning translucent and starting to brown, add the rest of the ingredients to the pan.

Simmer for 30–45 minutes until all the vegetables are soft. Remove from the heat and blend with a handheld blender until smooth. Season to taste and serve.

Mushrooms are a wonder food; they contain beta-glucans, which support the immune system, and onions are high in vitamin C and prebiotic fibre. This is a super-easy, non-blend soup.

Onion and porcini mushroom soup

Serves 4

2 large onions

olive oil, for frying

2 bay leaves

a handful chopped fresh sage (or 1 Tbsp dried sage)

50g dried porcini mushrooms (or other dried mushrooms), or 200g fresh mushrooms

1 litre boiling water or homemade vegetable stock

1 Tbsp miso paste

sea salt

Chop the onions and place in a large saucepan with a generous drizzle of olive oil and large pinch of salt. Fry over a medium heat for about 10 minutes until they start to soften, then add the bay leaves and sage and continue to fry for another 10 minutes until the onions start to brown.

Remove the bay leaves, chop then add the mushrooms and boiled water or vegetable stock and simmer for 20 minutes. Stir the miso into the soup just before serving; there is no need to blend.

Salads

Spelt is an ancient grain, lower in gluten than wheat. You could use barley instead if you prefer. Fresh cranberries are very high in antioxidants, but aren't available all year round, so redcurrants or blackcurrants are a good alternative during the summer. There is limited protein in this dish, so you may like to enjoy it with a small portion of meat or fish, or add a handful of chickpeas.

Kale, spelt and cranberry salad

Serves 2

100g (dry weight) pearled spelt
50g fresh cranberries
50g pecan nuts
¼ tsp ground allspice
1 Tbsp brown rice syrup
100g kale

Rinse the spelt and place in a small saucepan. Cover with cold water and bring to the boil. Simmer for 15–20 minutes, then remove from the heat and drain any excess water.

While the spelt is cooking, put the cranberries, pecan nuts, allspice and brown rice syrup in another small saucepan over a low heat. Stir gently until the syrup melts and covers the nuts and berries. Cook until the cranberries just begin to pop (this will take 8–10 minutes over a very low heat).

Meanwhile, roughly chop then steam the kale for just a couple of minutes.

Mix together the spelt, kale and nut-and-berry mixture, and serve warm.

The quinoa base of this salad is healthy and filling, but its subtle flavour does not detract from the wonderful fresh watercress and spring onion. Quinoa, a gluten-free seed, is a complete protein, which means it contains all of the essential amino acids. It is often described as a superfood.

This salad has a wonderful combination of different flavours, with the crunchy baked chickpeas adding a lovely bite. Watercress, being a bitter leaf, is good for stimulating digestion, while honey (be sure to use raw honey) has been found to have some potentially excellent health benefits due to its antioxidant content.

Quinoa, chickpea and watercress salad with pomegranate molasses

Serves 2

100g canned chickpeas (drained weight)

½ tsp paprika

100g quinoa (dry weight)

1 Tbsp pomegranate molasses

1 tsp raw honey

1 Tbsp balsamic vinegar

1 Tbsp olive oil, plus extra for roasting

2 handfuls of watercress

3 spring onions

sea salt

Preheat the oven to 200°C/gas mark 6.

Drain and dry the chickpeas as well as you can. Put them on a baking tray and drizzle with olive oil. Add a generous sprinkle of sea salt and toss around to coat. Roast in the oven for 20–30 minutes, shaking halfway through to ensure they roast evenly.

Remove from the oven and sprinkle over the paprika (always do this after roasting – if you do it before, the paprika can burn and taste bitter). Leave to cool. These crunchy chickpeas make a highly addictive snack, so you may want to make some extra!

Meanwhile, rinse the quinoa and place it in a saucepan. Cover with two times the volume of water. Bring to the boil, then reduce the heat to a gentle simmer and cook for 15 minutes, covered. Remove from the heat and leave for another 5 minutes, by which time all the water should have been absorbed. Set aside to cool.

In a small bowl or jug, mix together the pomegranate molasses, honey, balsamic vinegar and olive oil to make the dressing. Finely slice the spring onions, then toss the quinoa, watercress, spring onions and chickpeas together in a large bowl and drizzle the dressing over the top.

A simple salad with protein-rich black beans and seeds for some healthy fats. The rich colour of beetroot is down to its phytonutrients, including betalains, which have been found to be anti-inflammatory, and have benefits for heart health. Cooking destroys the phytonutrients, so for optimum health benefits, keep the beetroot raw! You can use cooked, canned black beans or cook them from dried. For the latter, soak overnight, then cook for about 40 minutes until soft and leave to cool. If you use canned, ensure you rinse them well.

Black bean and beetroot salad

Serves 2

1 large beetroot
1 large carrot
1 tsp honey
1 Tbsp olive oil
1 Tbsp cider vinegar
200g cooked black beans, drained
2 large handfuls mixed salad leaves
2 Tbsps pumpkin seeds (or mixed seeds)

Finely slice, spiralise or grate the raw beetroot and carrot.

Mix together the honey, olive oil and cider vinegar to make a dressing – I shake them all together in a small jar.

Arrange the mixed salad leaves, beetroot, carrot and beans on a large serving plate. Sprinkle over the seeds, drizzle over the dressing and serve.

Tip: If you prefer roasted beetroot, wrap your beetroot in foil with a good drizzle of olive oil and roast for about 1 hour at 160°C/gas mark 3. A knife should go in easily. Leave to cool, then peel away the skin and cut the beetroot into thin slices or small pieces.

A happy, healthy you

A delicious salad full of immune-boosting ingredients: quinoa (protein, vitamin E); mackerel (protein, vitamin D, omega-3 fatty acids); shiitake mushrooms (antiviral, antibacterial, antiparasitic, antifungal); parsley (vitamin A, vitamin C); kale (vitamin A, vitamin C); pumpkin seeds (zinc, essential fatty acids, protein); lemon juice and zest (vitamin C); and garlic (antiviral, antibacterial).

Immune-booster salad

Serves 2

90g quinoa (dry weight)

olive oil or coconut oil, for frying

100g fresh shiitake mushrooms (or other mushrooms of your choice)

2 garlic cloves

80g kale

zest and juice of ½ lemon

1 Tbsp balsamic vinegar

180g cooked mackerel

2 Tbsps pumpkin seeds

1 Tbsp freshly chopped parsley

Rinse the quinoa and place it in a saucepan. Cover with two times the volume of water. Bring to the boil, then reduce the heat to a gentle simmer and cook for 15 minutes, covered. Remove from the heat and leave for another 5 minutes, by which time all the water should have been absorbed. Set aside to cool.

Place a frying pan over a low–medium heat and add the olive oil or coconut oil. Chop the mushrooms into bitesize pieces and mince or finely slice the garlic. Gently fry together until the mushrooms have softened.

Roughly chop the kale, removing any stalks, then massage with the lemon juice to make it more digestible and add flavour. (Alternatively, you can briefly steam the kale if you find the raw vegetable unpalatable.)

In a large bowl, mix together the kale, quinoa, lemon zest, balsamic vinegar, mackerel (flaked into bitesize pieces), pumpkin seeds, mushrooms and garlic. Sprinkle over the fresh chopped parsley and serve.

This is a lovely fresh spring/summer salad, but do add a source of protein, such as some cold salmon or chicken, or a large handful of chickpeas, to turn it into a main meal. Pumpkin seeds are an excellent source of zinc, which is important for our immune system, and the three vegetables give a powerful dose of vitamin C.

Asparagus and radish salad with balsamic dressing

Serves 2–3

250g asparagus
1 tsp balsamic vinegar
1 Tbsp olive oil
1 Tbsp maple syrup
50g baby spinach
100g radishes
a handful of fresh mint, roughly chopped
20g pumpkin seeds

Fill a bowl with cold water and some ice cubes and keep to one side.

Cut the woody ends off the asparagus, then cut the spears in half.

Bring a saucepan of water to the boil and add the asparagus. Simmer for 4-5 minutes, then transfer the asparagus straight to the bowl of cold water so it doesn't continue to cook.

Cut the radishes into quarters.

In a small jug or jar, mix or shake together the balsamic vinegar, olive oil and maple syrup to make the dressing.

In a large bowl, toss together the baby spinach, asparagus, radishes and chopped fresh mint with the dressing. Top with the pumpkin seeds and serve.

A happy, healthy you

A wonderful selection of grains makes this salad healthy and interesting, but you could pick any one of them if you don't have all to hand. Quinoa and lentils are good sources of protein, and the wide variety of vegetables plus herbs makes for a salad high in antioxidants, vitamins, minerals and phytonutrients. Try to use good-quality, cold-pressed olive oil, which also contains health-benefiting polyphenols.

Raw vegetable wholegrain salad

Serves 2

50g brown rice

50g quinoa

50g split peas or dried lentils

1 Tbsp lemon juice

1 Tbsp tahini

1 tsp olive oil

75g cucumber

75g tomatoes

75g courgette

75g carrot

1 large handful (in total) of mixed fresh herbs (I recommend mint, parsley and chives), roughly chopped

sea salt

Rinse the rice and put in a tightly lidded saucepan or rice cooker. Add three times the volume of water to the pan. Cover and bring to the boil, then simmer, without removing the lid, for 30 minutes. Note, rice cookers may need different amounts of water and/or time.

Remove the pan from the heat while you prepare the salad.

When the rice has been cooking for about 15 minutes, rinse the quinoa and split peas or lentils and put them in another pan. Add enough water so that the water's volume is about twice that of the quinoa and lentils. Cover, bring to a simmer and cook for 15 minutes.

Place the lemon juice, tahini and olive oil in a small jar or jug with a pinch of sea salt and stir or shake to combine.

Dice the vegetables and roughly chop the herbs whilst the grains are cooking.

When the grains are all cooked, drain off any excess water (most should have been absorbed), mix them together and run under cold water in a sieve until cool. You can just set them aside to cool if you have time.

To serve, mix together the vegetables, herbs, dressing and grains in a large bowl and season further if required.

This is a very simple salad which is good alone or as a side, hot or cold. Wild rice is a source of fibre and protein, as are the broad beans. Thyme is a wonderful herb that has been found to have antifungal and antiseptic properties. In the winter, when apricots aren't available, segments of orange or chunks of pineapple make a good alternative.

Wild rice, broad bean, tofu and apricot salad

Serves 2

150g wild rice
1 Tbsp maple syrup
1 Tbsp olive oil
¼ tsp sea salt
1 sprig of fresh thyme, leaves removed, and stalk discarded
4 apricots
120g firm tofu
120g shelled broad beans

Rinse the rice and put in a tightly lidded saucepan or rice cooker. Add three times the volume of water to the pan. Cover and bring to the boil, then simmer, without removing the lid, for 30 minutes. Note, rice cookers may need different amounts of water and/or time.

Remove the pan from the heat while you prepare the salad.

In a small bowl or jug, mix together the maple syrup, olive oil, salt and thyme leaves to make a dressing.

Cut the apricots into quarters and the tofu into bitesize chunks. Grill together in a griddle pan, or under a hot grill for a couple of minutes each side, or until starting to brown.

Steam the broad beans for 2– 3 minutes – you want them to keep plenty of bite.

In a serving dish or large bowl, mix together the rice, apricot, tofu and broad beans, and drizzle over the dressing. Serve while still warm or allow to cool.

A happy, healthy you

This is a no-cook, super-quick salad that gives a great dose of good fats from the avocado, plenty of vitamins and minerals from the greens, and a good source of zinc from the pumpkin seeds and the prawns, a vital nutrient for immune system support. Make sure you use raw honey, which has antioxidant, antibacterial and antifungal properties.

Avocado and prawn salad with courgette ribbons

Serves 2

zest and juice of ½ lemon
1 tsp raw honey
1 Tbsp olive oil
½ courgette
1 avocado
80g mixed salad leaves
150g cooked prawns
a handful of pumpkin seeds

In a small bowl or jug, mix together the lemon zest and juice, honey and olive oil to make a dressing.

Finely slice or spiralise the courgette, chop the avocado and, In a large bowl or serving dish, gently toss in the dressing, together with the salad leaves, prawns and pumpkin seeds.

Pomegranate molasses is an ingredient that you may not have in your cupboard, but I'd highly recommend it! It transforms a dish without having to mix up lots of ingredients into a dressing and is fairly widely available in supermarkets. If you can't get any, try mixing sumac with some olive oil and balsamic vinegar instead.

Lentils are a good source of plant-based protein, and garlic is antiviral, so excellent for the immune system. The dish also contains a generous three portions of vegetables for a range of vitamins and phytonutrients.

Delicious hot or cold, this is a zero-effort salad that can be adapted to whatever vegetables you have to hand. It works well with a selection of winter root vegetables (parsnip, beetroot, etc.), or more of a summer mixture, like the one below. Peppers, fennel, sprouts and squash all work well too. Don't worry about exact quantities – just get a good selection in.

Puy lentil and roast vegetable salad

Serves 2

2 carrots

¼ red cabbage

1 courgette

½ aubergine

a handful of cherry tomatoes

2 garlic cloves

120g puy lentils (dry weight)

2 Tbsps lemon juice

2 Tbsps pomegranate molasses

2 Tbsps olive oil, plus extra for roasting

small handful of fresh mint leaves

Preheat the oven to 175°C/gas mark 4.

Chop the vegetables into large chunks (leave the tomatoes whole) and finely slice the garlic. Place on a baking tray and brush with a little olive oil. Roast for 30-40 minutes (make sure the aubergine is soft).

Meanwhile, rinse the lentils, then place them in a saucepan and cover with cold water. Place over a medium heat and simmer for 20 minutes, or until soft but firm. Drain off any excess water.

In a small bowl or jug, mix together the lemon juice, pomegranate molasses and olive oil to make a dressing. Finely chop the mint.

In a large bowl or serving dish, toss together the roast vegetables and lentils with the dressing and chopped mint. Serve hot or cold.

This is the perfect side for veggie burgers or grilled tofu, meat or fish, alongside a crunchy green salad. Gram for gram, herbs are some of the best sources of vitamins and minerals. If you can grow a few in pots or in the garden, even better! Tahini (sesame seed paste) is a good source of essential fatty acids, vitamin E and antioxidant lignans. It's a great store cupboard staple to have on hand for sauces, but it's also delicious served on crackers or with crudités.

Potato and fennel salad with tahini lemon dressing

Serves 4 as a side dish

500g potatoes
150g fennel bulb
2 Tbsps soy yogurt (or natural yogurt)
2 tsps tahini
½ tsp lemon juice
a handful of fresh parsley and/or chives
sea salt

If the potatoes are not baby ones, cut into bite-sized pieces. Steam or boil until cooked through, but not too soft (the time will really depend on the size of the potatoes). Rinse in cold water, then set aside to cool.

Thinly slice the fennel.

In a small bowl or jug, mix together the yogurt, tahini, lemon juice and a pinch of sea salt to make a dressing.

Arrange the potatoes and fennel in a serving bowl and gently mix in the dressing to lightly coat.

Roughly chop the herbs and sprinkle over the salad.

Main meals

Quinoa is a complete protein, meaning it contains all the essential amino acids that the body needs. Red cabbage is a cruciferous vegetable, high in cardioprotective anthocyanins, as well as glucosinolates, which research has shown may be helpful in fighting cancer. These burgers are stuffed with other nutrient-dense foods including antiviral garlic, immune-boosting mushrooms, and vitamin-rich sweet potato and apple.

Quinoa burgers with apple-braised red cabbage

Makes 4 burgers

For the cabbage

350g red cabbage

½ apple

100ml apple juice

2 Tbsps cider vinegar

For the burgers

100g quinoa (dry weight)

150g sweet potatoes

100g mushrooms

1 garlic clove

olive oil, for frying

1 Tbsp freshly chopped marjoram or parsley

1 heaped tsp wholegrain mustard

1 egg

sea salt and freshly ground black pepper

Finely slice the cabbage and the apple (you can leave the skin on). Put in a saucepan with the apple juice and vinegar and cook over a low to medium heat. Leave the lid on to keep the steam in the pan but if it looks like it is drying out, add a dash of water. Cook until really soft and the apple has broken down. This will usually take around 40 minutes.

Meanwhile, rinse the quinoa and put in a saucepan with enough water so that the water's volume is twice that of the quinoa. Place over a medium heat and bring to the boil, then reduce the heat to a gentle simmer and cook for 15 minutes with the lid on. Remove from the heat and leave for another 5 minutes. By now, all the water should have been absorbed.

Peel and chop the potatoes then boil or steam until soft. Drain and mash. Transfer the mashed potatoes to a large mixing bowl and add the quinoa. Leave to cool for at least 20 minutes.

Preheat the oven to 170°C/gas mark 3½ and line a baking tray with baking paper.

Chop the mushrooms finely, mince/finely chop the garlic and fry together in a little oil.

Once the mushrooms are just starting to brown, add to the bowl with the quinoa, potatoes, herbs and mustard then add the egg and season well. Mix to combine then form into patties and bake on a baking tray for 20 to 30 minutes until they are firm but not dried out.

Serve the burgers with the cabbage. Extra sautéed garlicky mushrooms on the side make a lovely addition.

This is a perfect, warming curry that is very easy to make and doesn't require an endless list of spices. Aubergines make a great base for curries as they soak up loads of flavour. The ginger adds a kick without making the dish too spicy, as well as being a nutritional powerhouse, and the cashews add a wonderful creamy nuttiness as well as a source of protein and essential fatty acids. If you like a spicier curry, you can add a tsp (or more) of chilli powder.

Aubergine and ginger curry

Serves 2

½ red onion

1 garlic clove

olive or coconut oil, for frying

1 thumb-sized piece fresh ginger

½ tsp ground turmeric

2 tsps curry powder

2 bay leaves

5 cardamom pods, gently crushed to open the husks

1 aubergine

1 large tomato

300ml vegetable stock

200ml coconut milk

50g cashews

150g wholegrain rice (dry weight)

sea salt

Prepare you vegetables to start; finely slice the onions, separately mince/finely chop the garlic and ginger and chop the tomato and aubergine into bite sized chunks.

In a large, heavy-based saucepan or casserole dish, fry the onion and garlic in a little oil and a generous pinch of salt for around 10 minutes until soft.

Add the garlic, ginger, turmeric, curry powder, bay leaves, cardamom, aubergine and tomato and stir to coat everything in the spices. Fry for a couple of minutes. Add the stock, coconut milk and cashews and stir well to combine. Cover and bring to a simmer over a medium heat. Reduce the heat to low and leave to simmer gently for about 30 minutes.

Meanwhile, rinse the rice and put in a tightly lidded saucepan or rice cooker. Add three times the volume of water to the pan. Cover and bring to the boil, then simmer, without removing the lid, for 30 minutes. Note, rice cookers may need different amounts of water and/or time.

Remove the pan from the heat while you prepare the salad (see Tip).

Remove the lid from the curry pan and increase the heat slightly for a further 10 minutes to allow the liquid to reduce and thicken a little if needed.

Serve with the cooked rice.

Tip: Adding ½ tsp ground turmeric, 1 bay leaf and 3–4 crushed cardamom pods to the rice while cooking will give it a lovely, complementary flavour.

Chickpea or lentil pasta is widely available from health food shops and larger supermarkets. They are gluten-free options and also good sources of plant-based protein. Avocado is a super source of healthy fats and makes the creamiest sauce. This is a great dish for young children.

Avocado and tahini pasta with courgette

Serves 2

150g chickpea or lentil
  pasta
1 avocado
juice of ½ lemon
1 Tbsp tahini
1 courgette, spiralised or
  finely sliced
sea salt

Optional toppings

fresh or sundried
  tomatoes, olives, herbs,
  pumpkin seeds

Cook the pasta according to the packet instructions. Whilst it is cooking, spiralise or finely slice the courgette and set aside. Mash the avocado with the lemon juice, tahini and a pinch of salt.

Add the courgette to the saucepan of pasta for the last 1–2 minutes of cooking. Drain, return to the pan and mix in the avocado sauce. Add any toppings and enjoy hot or cold.

A very speedy and simple curry that is mild, yet has plenty of richness from the creamy coconut spinach. Spinach is packed with nutrients and antioxidants including vitamin C and vitamin A. Cauliflower is a nutrient-rich cruciferous vegetable, and many of the spices have anti-inflammatory and immune-boosting properties. This dish is also delicious with the addition of prawns – add raw or cooked ones for a few minutes towards the end of cooking to heat through thoroughly, and benefit from the zinc shellfish contain, which is important for our immune systems.

Spinach and cauliflower curry

Serves 2

300g cauliflower (around ½ a medium head)

1 onion

2 garlic cloves

150g wholegrain rice (dry weight)

olive or coconut oil, for frying

1 tsp ground ginger, or a thumb-sized piece of fresh ginger, peeled and grated

4 cardamom pods, seeds only, crushed

½ Tbsp ground cumin

½ Tbsp ground coriander

½ tsp ground turmeric

¼ tsp ground black pepper

100g spinach

400ml can coconut milk

2 Tbsps ground almonds

Cut the cauliflower into bite size florets, finely chop the onion and mince/finely chop the garlic.

Meanwhile, rinse the rice and put in a tightly lidded saucepan or rice cooker. Add three times the volume of water to the pan. Cover and bring to the boil, then simmer, without removing the lid, for 30 minutes. Note, rice cookers may need different amounts of water and/or time.

Remove the pan from the heat while you prepare the salad.

Meanwhile, heat a little oil in a frying pan over a low heat and gently fry the onion until it is beginning to soften. Add the garlic along with all of the spices, stir, and cook for a few more minutes while you make the sauce.

In a separate pan, briefly heat the spinach until wilted, then blitz in a food processor (or with a handheld blender), with the coconut milk and ground almonds until you have a smooth, creamy sauce. Add this mixture to the pan with the onion mixture, and stir in the cauliflower florets. Cover and leave to cook for around 15 minutes. The cauliflower should be soft but not falling apart.

Serve with the rice and any curry extras you enjoy, such as a little lime pickle or mango chutney.

Tip: If you like more spice to your curries, add a whole green chilli with the cauliflower, then remove before serving.

A frittata is a quick and easy meal, and, just like omelettes and quiches, you can customise as much as you like, replacing the asparagus used here with any other vegetable you prefer. It is delicious served with a crispy green salad on the side. Asparagus, like most green vegetables, is nutrient-rich, and contains a phytonutrient called rutin, which may be anti-inflammatory and cardioprotective. I'm a big fan of eggs as a source of protein. Yes, you can eat them daily, and no, they won't raise your 'bad' cholesterol level!

Asparagus frittata

Serves 2

200g potatoes

3 spring onions

olive oil, for frying

150g asparagus

4 eggs

Small handful fresh herbs, chopped (e.g. parsley, marjoram, oregano, tarragon, chives)

sea salt and freshly ground black pepper

salad, to serve

Peel and dice the potatoes and boil or steam until just soft.

Slice up the spring onion and remove woody ends from the asparagus. Heat some oil in a deep frying pan over a medium heat. Add the spring onion and cooked potato. Allow to fry gently while you steam the asparagus in a steamer or separate pan for 3–4 minutes, until just tender (if your asparagus has thick stems, it may need slightly longer).

Beat the eggs and season with salt and black pepper. Mix in the fresh herbs, then pour the mixture over the potatoes and spring onions. Lay the asparagus stems over the top.

Cover the pan and leave to cook over a medium heat until there is no sign of raw egg on top (around 15-20 minutes depending on the depth of your pan). If need be, you can pop the pan under a medium–hot grill for 5 minutes to finish cooking and brown the top.

Serve the frittata with crispy green salad.

A happy, healthy you

Sweet potatoes have been found to contain significantly more fibre and vitamin C than regular potatoes. They are also a great source of beta-carotene, the plant form of vitamin A (it is converted in the body).

Lentils are a good source of plant-based protein, while the spices all pack a nutritional punch, with many being anti-inflammatory.

Sweet potatoes with tahini dressing and black dhal

Serves 2

2 medium-sized sweet potatoes

olive oil

mixed green salad, to serve

For the black dhal:

100g puy lentils (dry weight)

300ml vegetable stock

1 bay leaf

1 shallot (or ¼ onion)

1 garlic clove

½ tsp ground turmeric

½ tsp ground cumin

½ tsp ground coriander

½ tsp paprika

sea salt and freshly ground black pepper

For the tahini dressing:

2 Tbsps tahini

1 Tbsp tomato puree

1 Tbsp good-quality olive oil

1 Tbsp lemon juice

Preheat the oven to 190°C/gas mark 5.

Peel and finely chop the shallot and garlic.

Prick the sweet potatoes with a fork, brush with a small amount of olive oil and wrap in tin foil. Bake for about 45 minutes until the potatoes are soft on the inside and the skin is slightly crispy. Larger potatoes may need a little longer.

Meanwhile, make the dhal. Rinse the lentils thoroughly and put in a medium pan with the stock and bay leaf. Simmer over a medium heat while you cook the onions.

Heat a little oil in a small frying pan over a medium heat. Sauté the onion with a pinch of salt for a few minutes until softened, then add the garlic and cook for a further minute. Add the softened onions and garlic to the lentil pan, along with the spices. Cover and continue to cook over a medium heat for about 20 minutes until the liquid is soaked up and the lentils are very soft. Discard the bay leaf and season to taste.

Meanwhile, make the dressing by mixing together the tahini, tomato puree, olive oil and lemon juice in a small bowl or jug. You may need to add a couple of Tbsps of water for a more spoonable dressing.

When the baked sweet potatoes are ready, serve them alongside the dhal, with the dressing spooned over the top and green salad on the side.

Black beans are a good source of protein and various minerals including iron, zinc and magnesium. You may have noticed that darker vegetables and fruits contain more nutrients than light, and the same is true for beans, with black beans being at the top of the bean nutrient pyramid!

Black bean 'Bolognese'

Serves 4

1 small red onion

2 garlic cloves

80g mushrooms

olive oil, for frying

400g can cooked black beans, drained

400g can chopped tomatoes

1 tsp Worcestershire sauce

1 tsp tamari or soy sauce (tamari is gluten-free)

½ tsp ground cinnamon

1 tsp oregano or savoury (fresh or dried)

sea salt and freshly ground black pepper

baked potatoes (1 per person), or 300g spelt spaghetti, to serve

Finely chop the onion and mushrooms. Mince/ finely chop the garlic.

Heat a little olive oil in a large saucepan over a medium heat. Add the onion and cook for about 10 minutes until softened but not brown. Add the garlic and mushrooms and cook for another 5 minutes.

Add the black beans, tomatoes, Worcestershire sauce, soy sauce, cinnamon and herbs and mix. Cover and leave to simmer gently for about 30 minutes.

Meanwhile, prepare your baked potatoes or spaghetti.

Season the sauce to taste before serving.

A happy, healthy you

Pick a rainbow of vegetables for this super-quick dish to get a good range of phytonutrients, for example green pak choi (for glucosinolates), red peppers (very high in vitamin C) and orange carrots (for beta-carotene). Polenta makes a good gluten-free alternative to breadcrumbs or batter for a crispy finish.

Polenta-coated tofu (or chicken) with steamed vegetables and rice noodles

Serves 2

50g polenta

160g firm tofu or chicken breast

350g mixed vegetables

120g brown rice noodles

For the dressing

1 Tbsp toasted sesame oil

1 Tbsp miso paste

1 tsp fresh grated ginger

1 garlic clove

Cut the tofu/ chicken into strips. Place the polenta in a shallow bowl. Roll the tofu or chicken in the polenta to give each strip a thin coating (it should stick without any problem, but if it doesn't, brush a small amount of olive oil over and re-coat).

Finely slice or spiralise the vegetables and mince or finely chop the garlic.

Mix together the dressing ingredients (I find placing them all in a small jar and shaking well to combine works brilliantly).

Grill the tofu or chicken in a hot griddle pan, or under a hot grill, for about 3 minutes on each side. Ensure the chicken is cooked through.

Meanwhile, steam the vegetables for around 5 minutes (some vegetables may need a little longer) and cook the noodles according to the packet instructions.

Toss the noodles, vegetables and sauce together and serve topped with the crispy tofu or chicken.

Tip: If you don't have a steamer, placing a colander over a large saucepan works well (just put the saucepan lid on top). Alternatively, you can stir-fry the vegetables in a little olive oil or coconut oil.

You can, of course, use regular pasta for this dish, but a healthier option is to use lentil or chickpea pasta. Not only do these avoid refined grains and gluten, they are also a good source of protein. Homemade pesto is a favourite of mine. It's so easy to make and you can pack it full of nutrient-rich fresh herbs and leave out the excess salt that many shop-bought versions contain.

Pasta with wild garlic pesto and mushrooms

Serves 2

For the pesto

10g wild garlic

10g spinach

2 Tbsps olive oil

10g pumpkin seeds

10g pine nuts

large pinch of sea salt

olive oil, for frying

2 shallots, chopped

200g mixed mushrooms (a few shiitake will add a meaty, rich flavour, while porcini have a strong nutty taste)

150g lentil or chickpea pasta

sea salt

To make the pesto, simply blend together all of the ingredients until you have a fairly smooth mixture. This will last for a few days in the fridge in a clean, sealed container.

Heat a little olive oil in a frying pan over a medium heat and fry the shallots with a pinch of salt. Once softened, add the mushrooms. Don't let the get pan too hot (you don't want the oil to smoke) but do cook for long enough that the mushrooms reach an almost caramelising stage, which is where the flavour really comes out.

Meanwhile, cook the pasta according to the packet instructions.

Drain the pasta, stir in the pesto and top with the mushrooms and shallots. Quick and so simple!

A happy, healthy you

While wild garlic is delicious, it's not the easiest thing to get hold of and is very seasonal, so you can swap it (and the spinach) for basil to make a more traditional green pesto. Pumpkin seeds are a great source of zinc, and mushrooms, especially shiitake and some of the more exotic types that are increasingly available, contain beta-glucans, which are immunomodulating, so excellent for your immune system.

This is a really easy one-pot meal, perfect for when you are busy but need a healthy, filling dinner. I've already talked about the high fibre, vitamin C and beta-carotene in sweet potatoes. Chickpeas are a good source of protein and phytoestrogens, dried apricots are a great plant source of iron and the spices have anti-inflammatory properties. This is also a really comforting dish on a cold day!

Sweet potato and chickpea tagine

Serves 4

1 onion

olive oil, for frying

2 sweet potatoes (about 400g)

100g dried apricots

2 garlic cloves, crushed or finely chopped

240g canned chickpeas (drained weight)

400g can tomatoes

1 Tbsp maple syrup

1 Tbsp paprika

1 tsp ground ginger

½ tsp ground turmeric

½ tsp ground cinnamon

1 bay leaf

sea salt and freshly ground black pepper

brown rice, millet or couscous (if you aren't avoiding wheat), to serve

Chop the onion and fry in olive oil in a heavy casserole dish or chef's pan. After a few minutes add the chopped garlic.

Peel and chop the sweet potato into circa 2cm chunks and cut up the apricots into small pieces.

When the onion is soft, add all of the other ingredients along with 200ml water. Season and stir, then pop the lid on the pan and bring to a gentle simmer on a medium heat. Reduce the heat to fairly low and leave to cook, covered, for 30– 40 minutes, until the sweet potato is soft. You can pretty much leave this dish alone to cook, but give it a quick check after about 30 minutes and, if it is drying out but not cooked, add a splash more water.

Cook your chosen carbohydrate/grain according to packet instructions, and serve with the tagine.

Traditionally, shakshuka contains peppers, but this is a British spring version with spring greens (you can use sprout tops, kale or spinach if you prefer, all of which are cruciferous vegetables high in glucosinolates, important for supporting liver detoxification pathways). It is one of those meals that works at any time of day, from breakfast to dinner, and it is incredibly simple and quick to make. Turmeric is a powerful anti-inflammatory spice (use fresh if you can- peel and grate as you would fresh ginger) and needs black pepper to be fully absorbed by the body.

Simple shakshuka with spring greens

Serves 2

400g can chopped tomatoes

1 garlic clove, minced or finely chopped

½ tsp paprika

½ tsp ground turmeric

¼ tsp freshly ground black pepper

a handful of freshly chopped herbs (e.g. parsley, marjoram, oregano)

2 medium-sized potatoes

large handful spring greens or kale

2 Tbsps pine nuts

2 large eggs

chilli flakes, to taste (optional)

Put the tomatoes, garlic, spices and herbs in a shallow pan or cast iron pot with a lid over a medium heat and stir. Allow to simmer, uncovered, whilst you prepare the potatoes. Reduce the heat to low if it starts to bubble too much or dry out.

Dice the potatoes and steam or boil for a few minutes until almost soft enough to eat. Add to the tomato mix.

Chop the greens and add them to the dish, mixing them in so they are largely covered. Make two indents into the mixture and crack the eggs into them, then sprinkle over the pine nuts and chilli flakes (if using). Cover with the lid and cook until the eggs are done to your liking. Serve.

A happy, healthy you

Black beans are a great source of fibre, protein and various essential minerals, including iron and molybdenum, which is important for liver function. They go perfectly with this rich sauce, which contains anti-inflammatory ginger. And, of course, stir fries are a great way to consume a good selection of vitamin and phytonutrient-rich vegetables – try to pick a rainbow selection for optimum nutritional benefit.

Black bean and ginger stir fry

Serves 2

For the sauce

2 Tbsps tamari or
   soy sauce (tamari is
   gluten-free)

thumb-sized piece of
   fresh ginger, peeled
   and grated

2 tsps five spice paste or
   ground five spice

1 Tbsp coconut oil,
   melted

120g brown rice
   noodles

1 tsp coconut oil or
   olive oil

350g mixed vegetables,
   e.g. purple sprouting
   broccoli, kale, peppers,
   spring onions

400g can black beans
   (or 220g cooked black
   beans, if you prefer to
   cook your own)

Mix together the sauce ingredients in a small jug or bowl and set aside.

Finely slice or spiralise the vegetables and drain and rinse the beans. Cook the rice noodles according to the packet instructions (most take just a few minutes to cook). Drain and leave covered.

Heat the oil in a wok over a medium–high heat and add the vegetables, along with a splash of water (this will stop the oil getting too hot). Fry for about 5 minutes. Add the beans and half of the sauce and reduce the heat to medium–low. Continue to cook for another 5–10 minutes, until the vegetables are al dente.

Mix the rest of the sauce into the noodles and serve, topped with the vegetables and beans.

Brown rice and wild rice are filling, unrefined carbohydrates with a small protein component, while peas add additional protein to this dish. Fennel has beneficial effects for digestion, and pumpkin seeds are high in zinc, which is important for a healthy immune system. Lemon, as well as being an excellent source of vitamin C, is always a super way to add flavour without needing lots of salt or spice, and the capers add a lovely, vinegary element.

Fennel, lemon and tahini rice bowl

Serves 2

150g brown or wild rice

150g garden peas or petit pois

150g fennel

zest and juice of ½ lemon

1 Tbsp tahini

1 Tbsp extra-virgin olive oil

1 Tbsp freshly chopped tarragon

1 Tbsp capers

1 Tbsp pumpkin seeds

sea salt and freshly ground black pepper

Rinse the rice and put in a saucepan. Add enough water so that the water's volume is twice that of the rice, and cover tightly with a lid. Bring to the boil and simmer, without removing the lid, for 30 minutes. (If using a rice cooker instead, follow the manufacturer's instructions.) Allow to cool.

Steam or boil the peas for around 3 minutes and set them aside to cool (you can eat them raw, but this makes them a little more digestible).

Once you have cooked and cooled the rice, finely slice the fennel (I like to use a mixture of bulb and the green ends), and zest and juice the lemon (alternatively, you can use half a finely chopped preserved lemon).

Mix the tahini, olive oil, lemon zest and juice, tarragon and capers into the rice, season to taste, and serve in two bowls, topped with the fennel, peas and pumpkin seeds.

A happy, healthy you

The mixed beans in this chilli are a great source of protein, fibre and various minerals. Make sure you rinse them well to limit their bloating effects – you want there to be no bubbles left when you wash the beans. Tomatoes are high in lycopene, a powerful phytonutrient that has exhibited anti-cancer properties. The lycopene actually increases with cooking, so tomatoes are one of the few foods that are better for you cooked rather than raw. You can use any colour pepper you like, but red are the highest in vitamin C. Cacao has antioxidant properties and is high in magnesium; it also adds a lovely richness to the dish.

Easiest bean chilli

Serves 2

1 pepper (any colour)

½ medium onion

2 garlic cloves

1 tsp coconut oil or olive oil

400g can mixed beans

400g can chopped tomatoes

1 Tbsp smoked paprika

1 Tbsp cacao or cocoa powder

½ tsp cayenne pepper

sea salt or freshly ground black pepper

rice or a baked potato, to serve

Dice the pepper and finely chop the onion and garlic. Heat the oil in a large saucepan over a medium heat and add the onion, pepper and garlic. Fry for about 5 minutes until the onion has softened.

Drain and rinse the beans, then add them to the saucepan, along with the tomatoes, paprika, cacao and cayenne pepper. (You could also use chilli powder if you prefer – just adjust the quantity depending on how hot you like it. ½ tsp gives a mild heat.)

Simmer gently for about 20 minutes, until the mixture thickens slightly. Season with black pepper and a little sea salt if required, and serve with rice or a jacket potato.

This is a great, healthy alternative to traditional risotto. Buckwheat is actually a seed, not a grain, although it is generally treated as the latter. This does mean it is gluten-free, as well as being high in nutrients and fibre. Quinoa and millet are also both gluten-free and, combined, the three make for a great variety of fibre with lots of different prebiotics, which are essential for gut microbiome health. Edamame beans are a source of fresh soy, which is high in protein and phytoestrogens. Mint, as well as adding flavour, has antiseptic and antibacterial properties, and is good for digestion.

Three-grain egg and minted pea risotto

Serves 2

50g quinoa

50g buckwheat

50g millet

4 eggs

a handful of fresh mint
  leaves

1 Tbsp olive oil

1 tsp lemon juice

1 garlic clove, chopped

150g peas

150g edamame beans or
  shelled broad beans

sea salt and freshly
  ground black pepper

Rinse the quinoa, buckwheat and millet well, then place in a saucepan and add 400ml cold water. Bring to the boil, then reduce the heat to a simmer for 20 minutes until they are tender and most of the water is absorbed.

Meanwhile, hard-boil the eggs – medium–large eggs will take 8–10 minutes in boiling water. Once done, set the eggs aside until cool, then peel and cut into wedges.

Bash the mint leaves in a pestle and mortar with the olive oil, lemon juice, garlic and some sea salt and freshly ground black pepper.

When the grains are almost ready, add the peas and edamame beans to the pan and cook for a further 3–5 minutes. Drain off any excess water.

Mix together the grains, peas and mint dressing. Divide between two plates and top with the sliced eggs.

A happy, healthy you

A deliciously 'meaty' plant-based option, aubergines are a good source of fibre as well as B vitamins, and their dark purple skin is high in antioxidants. Do be aware, however, that aubergines are part of the nightshade family (like tomatoes), so are not so good for those on an anti-allergenic diet. The glaze is also very nutritious, with anti-inflammatory ginger and miso (a fermented soy paste), which is great for gut health.

Miso-glazed aubergine

Serves 2

1 large aubergine

1 tsp miso paste

1 tsp maple syrup

1 tsp tamari or soy sauce (tamari is gluten-free)

1 tsp grated fresh ginger

1 tsp olive oil

For the dipping sauce

2 Tbsps soy or natural yogurt

1 tsp tahini

1 tsp lemon juice

To serve

2 portions brown rice noodles

50g cashew nuts

1 Tbsp sesame seeds

freshly chopped coriander

handful of pomegranate seeds

Preheat the oven to 180°C/gas mark 4.

Cut the aubergine in half lengthways, then cut a criss-cross pattern into the inner side of each half (so the glaze can soak in).

In a small bowl, mix together the miso, maple syrup, soy sauce, ginger and olive oil and rub over the aubergine halves. Be generous with the amount of glaze!

Roast for about 40 minutes (this may vary depending on the size of the aubergine). The flesh should be very soft.

Meanwhile, mix together the yogurt, tahini and lemon juice in a small bowl.

The aubergines are delicious served over rice noodles, and topped with cashews, sesame seeds, pomegranate seeds and fresh coriander, with the dipping sauce on the side. It all makes for a wonderful combination of textures and flavours.

The salad here provides a great selection of vegetables high in vitamin C. Consuming some raw vegetables every day is very good for you, as most lose nutrients when cooked. Tofu is a good vegetarian protein (it's made from soy, which is high in phytoestrogens) but if you aren't a tofu fan, you could make this with chunks of chicken or beef. (Note: they will need longer cooking times than tofu, so adjust accordingly and ensure they are thoroughly cooked through before eating.)

Satay tofu with sweet and sour salad

Serves 2–3

For the salad

zest and juice of 1 lime

1 tsp maple syrup

½ tsp grated fresh ginger

1 Tbsp olive oil

½ bulb of fennel

1 carrot

1 red pepper

a handful of rocket

For the satay tofu

1 garlic clove

2 Tbsps smooth peanut butter

1 tsp maple syrup

1 Tbsp tamari or soy sauce (tamari is gluten-free)

50ml coconut milk

200g block of tofu, cut into 12 pieces

In a small bowl or jug, mix together the lime zest and juice, maple syrup, ginger and olive oil.

Finely slice the vegetables with a sharp knife or use a spiralizer, put in a large bowl, then pour over the dressing and mix well. Leave in the fridge until you are ready to eat. This is great made a little in advance so the dressing can soak into the vegetables.

For the satay, mix together the garlic (minced or finely chopped), peanut butter, maple syrup, soy sauce and coconut milk in a small bowl. Rub around half the paste over the tofu.

Thread the pieces onto skewers (this is optional – you can just pop them into a baking tray if you prefer) and cook under a hot grill, or on a hot griddle pan, for 3–5 minutes, turning after a couple of minutes.

Serve with the rest of the satay sauce and the salad. You could also add rice noodles for a more filling meal.

A happy, healthy you

Falafel makes a great on-the-go snack or lunchbox filler, as well as a main meal. I like to serve with plenty of salad or mixed roasted vegetables. Hummus or some dairy-free yogurt to dip into makes a delicious addition too. Chickpeas are a great source of fibre and protein, while the rich pigment of beetroot is down to its high levels of dietary nitrate, which research has found is particularly helpful for reducing blood pressure. Oregano is a powerful herb with antifungal, antibacterial and antiseptic properties.

Beetroot and carrot falafel

Makes about 10; serves 2–3

200g raw beetroot and/or carrot

400g can chickpeas (about 220g drained weight), plus 50ml of the liquid from the can (aquafaba)

1 garlic clove

1 Tbsp finely chopped fresh or dried oregano

olive oil (if frying)

sea salt and freshly ground black pepper

salad or mixed roasted vegetables, plus hummus or dairy-free yogurt, to serve

Grate the beetroot and/or carrot.

Drain the chickpeas (remembering to reserve the 50ml liquid), dry them as well as you can, and put in a large mixing bowl with the beetroot or carrot. Add the garlic (minced or finely chopped), along with the oregano and a generous pinch of sea salt and black pepper. Mash everything with a potato masher, until the chickpeas are broken down.

Mix in the chickpea liquid to bind the mixture together. Use your hands to form the mixture into 10 balls, then squash each one slightly to make rounded patties. You can either bake the falafel in a preheated oven at 180°C/gas mark 4 for 20 minutes, or fry in a little olive oil for 3–4 minutes on each side, until firm and turning golden.

Serve with salad and maybe a side of hummus or some dairy-free yogurt, for dipping.

This is a great dish when you want some comfort food, and it's much healthier than a Chinese takeaway! It's very adaptable, as you could replace the cauliflower and corn with other vegetables of your choice, chunks of tofu or chicken wings.

Sweet and sour vegetables with egg-fried rice

Serves 2

200g cauliflower

100g baby corn

150g wholegrain rice

olive oil, for frying

2 medium carrots

2 celery sticks

1 egg

a little chopped spring
onion, to serve

For the sauce:

50ml tomato puree

50ml apple cider
vinegar

2 Tbsps tamari or
soy sauce (tamari is
gluten-free)

1 Tbsp agave or brown
rice syrup

1 large garlic clove

generous squeeze of
lime juice

1 Tbsp cornflour mixed
with 1 Tbsp cold
water

Cut the cauliflower into bitesize florets, and cut the baby corn in half. Mince or finely chop the garlic.

Put the rice on to cook in a rice cooker or saucepan, following the packet instructions. Preheat the oven to 200°C/gas mark 6.

Meanwhile, put all of the sauce ingredients into a small saucepan over a low heat, except the cornflour and water mixture, and bring to a gentle simmer. Once it is gently simmering, add the cornflour and water mixture and stir in. Stir for a few minutes to allow the sauce to thicken a little.

Arrange the cauliflower and baby corn in a baking tray and pour over the sauce, coating them as well as you can. Put in the oven to roast for 20 minutes.

Heat a drizzle of olive oil in a large pan over a low heat. Finely dice the carrots and celery and gently fry.

When the rice is ready, stir it into the pan. Break in the egg, stirring immediately to coat.

Serve the cauliflower and baby corn over the egg-fried rice. A little spring onion is lovely sprinkled on top.

A happy, healthy you

Cauliflower is a cruciferous vegetable. These are nutritional powerhouses, high in vitamins A and C, as well as fibre, and glucosinolates, which research has found to have some fascinating cancer-supressing properties. Use raw apple cider vinegar for a shot of probiotic goodness, and plenty of garlic for its anti-inflammatory and immune-boosting effects.

Salmon is an oily fish, high in anti-inflammatory, cardioprotective omega-3 oils. I recommend eating oily fish twice a week. Celery isn't to everyone's taste, but cooking it makes it more palatable for many. It is high in fibre, vitamins, minerals and antioxidants, and has been shown to help with blood pressure regulation.

Warm celery, leek and bean salad with sesame-glazed salmon or tofu

Serves 2

1 Tbsp sesame seeds

1 Tbsp cornflour

1 tsp toasted sesame oil, plus extra to serve

2 salmon fillets (or 2 x 100g blocks of firm tofu)

2 celery sticks

1 large leek

olive oil, for frying

100g (drained weight) cooked cannellini beans

sea salt and freshly ground black pepper

Preheat the oven to 180°C/gas mark 4.

In a small bowl, mix together the cornflour, sesame seeds and sesame oil with a little seasoning to form a paste. Rub over the top of the salmon or tofu.

Chop the celery into chunks and slice the ends and leafy tops off the leek, then cut into rounds. Pan fry the leeks and celery together over a medium heat in a little olive oil with a generous pinch of salt.

Pop the salmon or tofu into the oven once the vegetables are cooking. The cooking time for salmon will vary depending on the size of your fillets and how well-done you like it. Personally, I like my salmon slightly undercooked in the middle, so for an average fillet (about 120g), I cook it for about 8–10 minutes. The tofu will need 15 minutes.

When the vegetables are just about cooked, add the cannellini beans to heat through, then serve the salmon or tofu on the bed of vegetables and beans, with a drizzle of sesame oil.

Noodle bowls are a favourite dinner in our house as they are so quick and easy to make, full of flavour and nutrient-rich! This is an incredibly versatile dish as you can add whatever vegetables you like; anything that you'd put in a stir fry will generally be suitable. Sometimes I add a handful of herbs too; coriander and basil are particularly good, both for flavour and for their antibacterial/anti-inflammatory properties. This is quite a good dish for those with a low appetite, as you can always just sip on the broth. Use full-fat coconut milk to get plenty of calories.

Vegetable and prawn coconut noodle soup

Serves 2

1 Tbsp coconut oil

200g mixed crunchy vegetables (e.g. carrots, fennel, cabbage, celery, courgettes, peppers, broccoli)

200ml vegetable stock

400ml coconut milk

½ –1 small chilli (depending on how spicy you like your food!), finely chopped

1 garlic clove

thumb-sized piece of fresh ginger, peeled and grated

1 stick lemongrass

150g uncooked king prawns (you can swap these for stir-fried pieces of tempeh, tofu or meat)

100g rice noodles (this dish works well with fine vermicelli noodles or larger udon noodles)

25g cashew nuts

a handful of herbs – I recommend coriander and basil

a squeeze of fresh lime

Cut up your vegetables. You don't want anything too chunky so ribbons and thin slices work best. Mince or finely chop the garlic.

Heat the coconut oil in a wok over a medium heat. Add the vegetables and fry for around 10 minutes. Once they are turning tender and browning a little, add the stock and coconut milk, along with the chilli, garlic, ginger and lemongrass. Stir together and leave to simmer for 15–20 minutes.

Meanwhile, prepare the noodles according to the packet instructions.

Add the prawns to the wok and cook for about 3 minutes. Make sure they are all submerged in the liquid so that they cook evenly. They should be completely pink all the way through, with no grey flesh left.

Divide the noodles between two large bowls, then ladle on the soup (discarding the lemongrass). Sprinkle the cashews and herbs on top, and finish with a generous squeeze of fresh lime over each bowl.

A happy, healthy you

Salmon is an oily fish high in omega-3 essential fatty acids. Although fresh is generally best, I like keeping a can of salmon in the cupboard for instant meals. The accompanying salad contains leaves high in vitamin C and K, and its bitter flavours stimulate digestive enzymes, so are particularly good for those who struggle with digestive issues. For an extra nutrient kick, you can use sweet potatoes instead of regular. These are high in beta-carotene, the plant form of vitamin A.

Salmon fishcakes with bitter salad

Serves 2–3

250g potatoes

75g baby spinach

160g can cooked salmon or 1 fresh fillet, cooked and flaked

50g chickpea flour (you can use other types of flour if you prefer)

1 tsp freshly chopped dill

zest and juice of 1 lime

1 heaped Tbsp capers, chopped

2 eggs

2 Tbsps polenta

For the salad

2 Tbsps soy or natural yogurt

50g watercress, roughly chopped

50g rocket, roughly chopped

50g baby spinach, roughly chopped

Peel and chop the potatoes. Bring a saucepan of water to the boil and add the potatoes. Boil for until soft (around 20 minutes depending on their size). During the last couple of minutes, place a steamer basket (a colander also works well) over the top of the pan and use it to wilt the spinach. Drain the potatoes, then mash with the spinach and leave to cool.

Preheat the oven to 170°C/gas mark 3½.

Add the salmon, flour, chopped capers and dill to the potato mix, along with half the lime zest and juice. Break in one of the eggs and mix well to combine. Use your hands to form the mixture into six medium-sized patties (that can easily fit in your palm).

In a small bowl, beat the other egg. Put the polenta in a shallow dish or plate. Roll each fishcake in the egg, followed by the polenta to coat. If you want to prep ahead, you can refrigerate them for up to 12 hours until ready to cook.

Put the fishcakes on a baking tray and bake in the oven for 25 minutes.

For the salad, mix the yogurt with the rest of the lime zest and juice in a small jug or bowl. In a large bowl, mix the watercress, spinach and rocket with the dressing and serve with the fishcakes.

Tip: As an alternative to the salad, peas and cooked spinach are a great accompaniment to these fishcakes.

While only a nod to traditional kedgeree, this is a deliciously comforting dish. It's particularly good when you feel like stronger flavours, which can sometimes be the case while on medications that numb taste buds.

Mackerel is an oily fish and a great source of anti-inflammatory omega-3 essential fatty acids. Fish is also one of the best dietary sources of vitamin D, which is essential for our immune system. Turmeric is a powerful anti-inflammatory spice, and cinnamon has been found useful in helping balance blood glucose levels.

Buckwheat kedgeree

Serves 2

120g buckwheat

150g peas (fresh or frozen)

2 eggs

olive or coconut oil, for frying

1 medium onion

1 tsp turmeric

1 tsp cinnamon

1 tsp garam masala

¼ tsp freshly ground black pepper

180g smoked mackerel, skin removed, flaked into bite-sized pieces

few sprigs fresh parsley, to serve

Put the buckwheat in a saucepan and cover in cold water. Place over a medium heat, bring to the boil, then simmer for 15–20 minutes until soft but not soggy. Add the peas for the last five minutes. Drain off any excess water.

Meanwhile, in a separate pan, boil the eggs to either medium- or hard-boiled, depending how you like them (medium–large eggs will take 8–10 minutes to hard-boil). Plunge the eggs into cold water for a couple of minutes, then set aside.

Remove the skin from the fish and flake into bite size pieces and set aside.

Place a frying pan over a medium heat and add a little olive or coconut oil. Finely chop the onion and fry until soft and just starting to brown. Add the spices to the pan, along with the cooked buckwheat and peas, and the mackerel. Stir to combine and fry for a few minutes while you peel the eggs and chop them in half.

Serve topped with the eggs and a sprinkle of parsley.

A happy, healthy you

Salmon is a great source of omega-3 essential fatty acids, which are important anti-inflammatory nutrients. Red peppers are a super source of antioxidants, including vitamin C and beta-carotene, as well as fibre. Quinoa is one of the only plant-based 'complete' proteins, containing all the essential amino acids (protein building blocks) the body needs.

Salmon and quinoa stuffed roasted peppers

Serves 2

2 red peppers

olive oil, for baking/ frying

100g quinoa

½ medium aubergine

150g cooked salmon fillet, flaked

zest of 1 lemon

1 Tbsp capers

a handful of freshly chopped parsley

sea salt

mixed salad, to serve

Preheat the oven to 180°C/gas mark 4.

Cut the tops off the peppers and remove the seeds. Brush the peppers and their tops all over with a little oil, then place them cut-side down on a baking tray. Roast in the oven for 15 minutes. Remove and allow to rest until cool enough to handle. Do not switch off the oven.

Meanwhile, put the quinoa in a medium saucepan and add enough water so that the water's volume is twice that of the quinoa. Place over a medium heat and bring to a simmer, then cover with a lid, reduce the heat to low and cook for 15 minutes. By now it should have absorbed all the water. Turn the heat off and leave to sit with the lid on for a further 5 minutes.

While the quinoa is simmering, finely dice the aubergine and heat a little oil in a small frying pan over a low–medium heat. Add the aubergine and a good pinch of salt and lightly fry for about 15 minutes until the aubergine is browned all over and tastes cooked through.

Mix the cooked quinoa with the flaked salmon, cooked aubergine, lemon zest, capers and parsley.

When the peppers are cool enough to handle, stuff them with the mixture, top with their lids and return to the oven to roast for a further 15 minutes. You will probably have some excess mixture, so just place it around the peppers to cook, drizzling with a little olive oil so it doesn't dry out.

Serve with a mixed salad.

Although probably not the most popular of fish, sardines are a wonderful source of omega-3 essential fatty acids and the tinned ones are a great staple item to keep in the cupboard. While they can have quite a strong flavour, mashing them into potatoes with lemon and sour cream makes them very palatable.

Fishy loaded potato skins

Serves 2

2 baking potatoes

olive oil, for drizzling

1 can tinned sardines (drained weight 80–100g)

1 Tbsp dairy-free crème fraîche (or soy or natural yogurt)

4 spring onions

squeeze of fresh lemon juice

a couple of large sprigs of fresh parsley or dill

salad or vegetables of your choice, to serve

Preheat the oven to 180°C/gas mark 4.

Rub the potatoes with a drizzle of olive oil, wrap in foil and bake in the oven for around 40 minutes, until soft inside. Larger potatoes may need a little longer.

Finely chop the spring onion and herbs.

Once baked, cut the potatoes into halves or quarters and scoop out most of the flesh. In a bowl, mash the removed flesh with the sardines, crème fraîche, spring onion, lemon juice and herbs, then refill the skins. Pop them back in the oven for another 10 minutes to make them slightly crunchy on the outside.

Serve with plenty of salad or mixed steamed vegetables.

A happy, healthy you

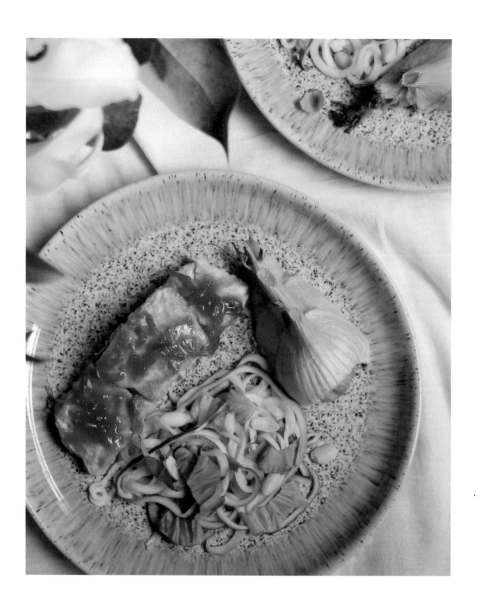

Salmon is a super, oily fish, high in anti-inflammatory omega-3 essential fatty acids. This sweet chili sauce adds lovely flavour without all the nasties that come with many bottled sauces. Fennel and courgettes are two good summer vegetables, but you can have the salmon alongside any others you fancy. A baked sweet potato, high in fibre and vitamin A, also goes well with this dish.

Sweet chilli salmon

Serves 2
2 salmon fillets
½ fennel bulb
olive oil, for baking
1 courgette
a few basil leaves

For the sweet chilli sauce (makes more than enough for 2)
50g (about ¼) red onion
olive oil, for frying
1 garlic clove
2 Tbsps brown rice syrup or soft brown sugar
1 tsp apple cider vinegar
up to ¼ tsp dried chilli flakes or finely chopped fresh chilli (depending on the strength of your chillies and how spicy you like it!)
1 tsp cornflour mixed with 1 tsp water

Preheat the oven to 180°C/gas mark 4.

Begin by making the sweet chilli sauce (which can be made in advance). Chop the onion very finely then heat a little olive oil over a low heat in a small saucepan. Add the onion and fry for around 15 to 20 minutes until really caramelised. It should go translucent, then sticky and a little brown, but be careful not to burn it. Add the garlic (minced or finely chopped) to the onions just as they show the first signs of browning. Fry for a couple more minutes, then take off the heat.

In a separate small saucepan, over a low heat, mix together the syrup or sugar and vinegar until the sugar dissolves, then add the chilli. Slowly add the cornflour and water mixture, stirring continuously as the sauce thickens. Remove from the heat as soon as it has thickened, then mix in the onions and garlic and set aside until needed. The sauce lasts well over a week in a clean, sealed container in the fridge.

When you're ready to cook, rub a generous amount of the sweet chilli sauce over the two salmon fillets (you can use it all or keep a little back to add at the end), then wrap them loosely in foil and place on a baking tray. Cut the fennel into large chunks and brush with a little olive oil, then add to the baking tray. Bake for about 20 minutes (the exact cooking time will depend on the thickness of your salmon fillets and how well you like them cooked).

When the salmon is nearly done, spiralise (or finely slice) the courgette and steam in a lidded pan (a colander over a large saucepan works well if you don't have a steamer basket) for a few minutes, then toss together with the roughly chopped basil leaves and a generous drizzle of olive oil.

Serve the salmon and roasted fennel on the courgetti bed.

Sweet Treats

These are great to suck on if you feel nauseous or have mouth sores from treatment.

Rather than buying ready-made lollies laden with sugar and additives, try making your own. You'll need lolly moulds, but these are inexpensive and widely available (make sure it is BPA-free). Quantities will depend on the size of your moulds, but most will hold around 75–100ml each.

Fruit lollies

coconut water, diluted fruit juice or watered-down natural yogurt (roughly one part water to three parts yogurt)

finely chopped berries or other soft fruits (peaches, nectarines, etc.)

Simply pop the fruit into the moulds until they are about a third full, then top up with your chosen liquid and freeze overnight.

Great for a snack or dessert, these jellies contain the most unusual ingredient of all the recipes in this book – agar flakes! Don't be put off; they are found in most health food stores and a number of larger supermarkets, and they last ages in the cupboard.

Natural fruit jelly

Serves 6

360ml apple juice

1½ Tbsps agar flakes

large handful of berries or other chopped fruit (but not pineapple, kiwi or papaya, which contain enzymes that will stop the jelly setting)

Put the apple juice in a small saucepan over a medium heat and sprinkle the agar over the top. Bring to the boil without stirring. Once boiling, reduce the heat to a gentle simmer and stir until the agar is dissolved (this doesn't take long). Remove from the heat.

Divide the fruit between six ramekin dishes and pour over the liquid. Leave to cool to around room temperature, then put in the fridge overnight to finish setting.

A happy, healthy you

The oat-and-nut topping makes a good alternative to refined flour and adds a little protein. The brown sugar is optional, so leave it out if you are on a very low sugar diet. Sweet spices like cinnamon are great to add to reduce the need for lots of sugar, and cinnamon has various health benefits, including being good for helping to balance blood sugar levels, but you could use ginger, mixed spice or nutmeg instead.

Quick fruit crumble

Serves 4

100g jumbo oats

50g ground almonds

1 tsp cinnamon

20g coconut oil, melted

300g poached/lightly cooked fruit (e.g. apple, pear, rhubarb, etc. – see Tip) or uncooked berries

50g brown sugar, optional

Preheat the oven to 175°C/gas mark 3½.

Mix together the oats, almonds, cinnamon, coconut oil and sugar (you can just rub them together in a bowl using your hands or use a stand mixer).

Put the fruit into an ovenproof bowl or pie dish and top with the crumble mix, pressing it down lightly with your hands or a wooden spoon.

Bake for 30 minutes and serve.

Tip:
To poach fruit, peel it and cut into bite-sized pieces. Put in a saucepan with a splash of water and simmer gently until the fruit is soft. The amount of time will depend on the fruit you choose. You want the fruit to be reasonably wet so the crumble as a whole isn't dry. If it seems quite dry, add a splash of fruit juice.

A happy, healthy you

A low-sugar dessert that is warming and comforting in winter. You can leave out the syrup if you're on a very low sugar diet. Citrus fruit is high in vitamin C and beta-carotene, both antioxidants.

Citrus-topped rice pudding

Serves 4

100g pudding rice

50ml maple or agave syrup

700ml coconut or almond milk

generous pinch of grated nutmeg

seeds of 3 cardamom pods, ground

2 oranges (regular or blood oranges)

Preheat the oven to 150°C/gas mark 2.

Put the rice into an ovenproof dish. Pour over the syrup and milk and sprinkle over the nutmeg and cardamom. Cover with a lid or tinfoil and bake in the oven for around 1 hour. The shape and type of dish will cause the cooking time to vary, so keep an eye on it and, if it seems too loose, pop it back in for another 10–15 minutes. When it's ready, the rice should be swollen and firm enough that you can put the orange slices on top without them completely sinking in.

Peel and thinly slice the oranges. When the pudding is ready, remove it from the oven, stir, then layer the orange slices over the top.

Return to the oven for another 30 minutes, uncovered. The pudding should be firm but not dry. Serve.

This is a lovely, comforting dish and ginger can really help with nausea, as well as being anti-inflammatory and containing antioxidants. Pears are a good source of dietary fibre and vitamin C. You can also make this dish with plums (a good seasonal summer alternative).

Pears poached in spiced ginger syrup

Serves 4

4 pears

100ml maple syrup

1 stick of cinnamon

1 thumb-sized piece of fresh ginger

Peel the pears but leave the core intact. Peel the ginger and grate.

Put everything into a small saucepan with 100ml water. Place over a low–medium heat and cover. Leave to simmer for 45 minutes (reduce the heat if the liquid goes beyond a very gentle simmer), turning the pears every 15 minutes to ensure they cook through.

Remove the pears and set aside. Increase the heat to high and boil the liquid, uncovered, for 5–10 minutes until it reduces by approximately half.

Remove the syrup from the heat and let it cool for a few minutes before pouring it over the pears to serve.

A seemingly unhealthy dessert is given a healthier twist here, low in sugar and dairy-free. You can also swap the rhubarb for soft mixed berries, in which case leave out the maple syrup, as these are naturally sweeter than rhubarb.

Rhubarb fool

Serves 6

400g rhubarb

50ml elderflower cordial (other sweet fruit or ginger cordials also work well)

½ tsp cinnamon

50ml maple syrup

200ml oat cream

100ml soy or coconut yogurt

Chop the rhubarb into circa 2cm pieces and put into a shallow pan with half of the elderflower cordial, along with the maple syrup and cinnamon. Place over a low heat and poach for about 20 minutes until the rhubarb is soft and falling apart. Break it up gently with a wooden spoon. Set aside to cool completely, then put in the fridge. Leave for up to 24 hours.

Whisk together the oat cream and yogurt with the rest of the cordial, then gently fold in the cold rhubarb. You can leave for a few more hours in the fridge until you are ready to eat.

This makes a great dessert, snack, or even make-ahead breakfast. You can swap the rice syrup for maple syrup or honey, if you prefer. If using honey, try to get raw, which contains antioxidants. Cook it on the lowest heat you can, though, or these will be damaged by the heat.

Creamy pumpkin layer puddings

Serves 4

For the pumpkin layer

400g pumpkin flesh (or a can of pumpkin puree)

70ml brown rice syrup

1 tsp cinnamon

For the oat layer:

80g jumbo oats

60ml brown rice syrup

100ml oat cream

Deseed, remove the skin and chop the pumpkin into chunks. Put the pumpkin in a saucepan with the brown rice syrup, cinnamon and about 30ml water. Cover and cook over a low heat for 20–30 minutes, until the pumpkin is very soft. Add a splash more water if it starts to dry out, but the pumpkin should have enough natural juices without this.

Leave the stewed pumpkin to cool, then puree with a handheld blender. Divide the mixture between four serving glasses, then leave to cool completely. If you're using pumpkin puree, simply mix it with the syrup and cinnamon, then divide between glasses. There is no need to add water.

In a small pan over a low heat, put the oats and brown rice syrup and stir together until the rice syrup is melted and just starting to bubble, and the oats are covered. Remove from the heat and leave to cool.

Pour a layer of oat cream over the pumpkin, then divide the sweet oat mixture between the glasses. Don't worry if it sinks into the oat cream a little! Serve and enjoy.

A happy, healthy you

These are good for an energy boost or for those struggling with keeping weight on, as they are calorie- and nutrient-dense. Seeds are high in essential fatty acids, dry fruit is a good source of fibre, and raw cacao is surprisingly high in antioxidants!

Raspberry seed bars

Makes around 12 bars

50g dates or dried figs

175g mixed seeds (e.g. sunflower, pumpkin, sesame or chia)

2 Tbsps coconut oil

2 Tbsps raw cacao powder (you can use cocoa powder instead)

2 Tbsps maple syrup

2 Tbsps nut butter (any kind)

50g fresh or frozen raspberries

100g dark chocolate, broken into pieces (try to use one that is at least 70 per cent cocoa. Don't worry if you usually find that too bitter, the rest of the bar is sweet enough)

Line a shallow 20cm baking tin with baking parchment (this will make it much easier to get the bars out).

Finely chop the dates or figs. Place all the ingredients except the raspberries and chocolate in a small saucepan over a low heat. Stir gently until the coconut oil has melted and the seeds and fruit are well coated. Take off the heat and stir in the raspberries, allowing them to crush a bit as you do so. Press the mixture into the prepared tin.

Place the chocolate in a bowl set over a small saucepan of simmering water (try not to let the bowl touch the water). Once the chocolate has melted, pour it over the seed mixture and smooth over the top.

Refrigerate for at least 1 hour until firm, then remove from the tin and cut into slices or pieces. Store in the fridge until you are ready to eat.

*'Do something
today that
your future
self will
thank you for'*

Part five:

Be the happiest, healthiest you

I hope that my story, and the tips and recipes in this book, have been useful to you. As a little summary, these are the things I'd like you to take away to think about:

- Ask yourself the big life questions of what makes you happy or not, and what you can do to live the life you'd like to live.
- See something positive in every day (but allow yourself down days too).
- Value your body and nourish it in every way you can; make little healthy adjustments to your life and home over time.
- Enjoy good food and fill yourself with nourishment!

I want to end with a letter I wrote to all my friends and family the Christmas after my diagnosis, because without them, I wouldn't be as happy as I am, and without many of them, this book would not exist! I wanted everyone to know how grateful I was for my life so far, and how I was still able to live a happy life despite everything. I hope you get a little inspiration from this, and the rest of my book, to look at the good things in your life, and find a way to be the happiest and healthiest you.

To all the special people in my life,

Thank you. For the good times we've had together. For the times we've laughed, or cried, or worked or danced together. I am 34, far too young to be faced with a terminal illness, yet I feel like I've packed so much into my life already, and that's in huge part thanks to all of you. And that makes me grateful and happy and in some small way, helps me make peace with what I'm facing.

To my family and family-in-law: you are incredible, and I am so grateful to have you all. Whatever happens in the future, I get so much comfort knowing that Brian and Oscar have you all in their lives.

To those I've known since childhood: thank you for staying friends and supporting me as I grew up. From pony-loving little girl, to angsty teen, through my career-obsessed twenties burning the candle at both ends, to a happy and balanced wife and mum in my thirties. I've grown and changed and discovered, and you've been there along the way.

To friends from school and university – we've had a lot of laughs! My Trent girls: it's a huge testament to all of us that we are still close. From giggles in Martin, to meet-ups with our growing gaggle of babies. I feel stronger knowing you lot have got my back. Uni friends, college, rowing and miscellaneous others(!), we drank and danced and survived all-night essay writing. Some of you have become my closest friends; friends I truly could not imagine my life without. Friends who offer a shoulder to cry on, words of wisdom, a good gossip or just quiet company when I need it.

To all those colleagues who've crossed that line into friendship: thank you for helping me achieve success in my career, for being there when it got too stressful at times, and for both challenging and supporting me. While I've left behind my City days, I'm proud of how much I achieved and how hard I worked, and so grateful for all the amazing people I met and worked with along the way.

And to everyone who doesn't fit into the above: housemates I've shared so much with; friends of friends, who, over the years have become firmly my friends too; friends of Brian who've welcomed me with open arms; my new mum friends who kept me sane when Oscar was tiny, and who I feel like I've known for far longer than I have; and my wonderfully caring college friends, who share my passion for health and helping others. Thank you all for being a part of my life, for bringing joy and fun and love and support.

I hope this Christmas is wonderful for you, and 2019 brings much happiness. I hope that I will be seeing lots of you next year and for many years to come, but whatever the future brings, know that I am grateful for my past, and that you've been part of it.

With the biggest hug and all my love,

Caroline ♡

A happy, healthy you

Recipe index

A happy, healthy you

A happy, healthy you

Thanks

This book wouldn't have been possible without an amazing team of people helping me out. Thanks to every single one of you who helped with recipe testing, proofreading and offering general advice.

Particular thanks must go to:

General all-round rock and supporter
My darling husband Brian

Illustrations
Lisa Huxley-Blythe

Photography and recipe testing
Aimee Twigger @twiggstudios
Annika Patel @coniferesetfeuillus
Ceri Jones @cerijoneschef
Esha Sachdeva @delusciousbites
Eva Dillitz @sunfoodstories
Hana Mendes @nirvanacakery
Irina Georgescu @irina.r.georgescu
Joanne Wood @the_balanced_kitchen
Lucy Parissi @supergolden88
Monisha Sharma @monsflavors
Nicky Corbishley @kitchensanctuary
Rebecca Goodman @figsandpigsinsta
Samantha Hadadi @samanthahadadi
Shahla Rashid www.myberkeleykitchen.com
Shilpa Razniewska @soulful_and_healthy
Véronique Sampson @applesandguavas